Wynifried Tennyson Jesse was born at Chislehurst, Kent in 1888. She early learned from her father, a chaplain, her love of travel, and was to live in places as distant as St Tropez and Cornwall, Hollywood and London.

She did not become known as Fryn until, at eighteen, she began her four years at the Forbes's Newlyn School of Painting. There she first displayed only some of the talents which were to distinguish her as one of the most gifted women of her generation. These included not only fiction, but also journalism (notably for *The Times* and the *Daily Mail*, where she was one of the few women to report from the Front), illustration (one commission was the interior decoration of the Ambassador's Theatre), and playwriting. All nine of her plays were produced in the West End, six being collaborations with H. M. Harwood. Their first, an adaptation of her famous story 'The Mask' (1912) – which went on to be filmed and, like *A Pin to See the Peepshow*, televised – led to their secret marriage in 1918. In addition, she wrote three short-story collections, nine novels (including, in 1929, her classic *The Lacquer Lady*), poetry, belles lettres, and a history of Burma. She was also a brilliant criminologist and, following publication of her highly acclaimed *Murder and its Motives* (1924), edited six Notable British Trials.

Despite her prodigious canon, her popularity and her great beauty, she suffered (like her great-uncle before her) from crippling depression throughout her life. She died in London in 1958.

THE
BAFFLE BOOK

Lassiter Wren
and
Randle McKay

Edited by
F. Tennyson Jesse

Illustrated with Diagrams and Charts

THE HOGARTH PRESS
LONDON

Published in 1984 by
The Hogarth Press
40 William IV Street, London WC2N 4DF

First published in Great Britain by William Heinemann 1930
Hogarth edition offset from original Heinemann edition
Copyright the Estates of the Authors
Copyright the edited version the Literary Estate of F. Tennyson Jesse, 1958

British Library Cataloguing in Publication Data

Wren, Lassiter
The baffle book.
1. Puzzles
I. Title   II. MacKay, Randle
III. Jesse, F. Tennyson
793.73   GV1493

ISBN 0 7012 1921 1

Printed in Great Britain by
Cox & Wyman Ltd
Reading, Berkshire

What Is Your Score

for THE BAFFLE BOOK?

Score your credits here. A total of 150 is good. 200, excellent. 250, remarkable. 280 (maximum), amazing!

Carry forward ......

Answers to the questions printed at the end of each problem will be found in the Answer Section, printed upside-down in the back of the book.

The highest possible score is 280—that is, 10 credits each for the 28 mysteries or detective problems.

PREFACE

THE Baffle Book is not a collection of short stories. It is a parlour game, and a very good game, too. Its originators, Mr. Lassiter Wren and Mr. Randle McKay, explain in their foreword how it is to be played.

My own very small share in the book has been to transpose some of the cases to make them intelligible to the English reader who does not know the United States. I do not mean that I have necessarily removed the setting of all the cases from America to Europe. Some were set in Europe already, and three or four, such as " The Lighthouse Tragedy," " The Club Car Mystery," and " The Elevated Transit Mystery," were obviously insusceptible to transportation. In the two latter cases I have simply inserted some explanatory matter necessary for the majority of English readers. Wherever possible I have changed the locality to England, with corresponding necessary alterations in the details, and perhaps even in the nature of the crime, simply because it is easier for the mind and imagination to work amongst scenes and circumstances that are known.

Obviously in a book of this kind the finer points of detection—those based on knowledge of character—have to be abandoned. The psychical interest of crime detection lies in the ability to deduce from knowledge of a suspect's character what he would or would not do, and that is why the better the writer, the better the detective story.

What a superb detective writer of the psychical sort would Jane Austen have been! How well we should have been able to deduce, simply through the insight she gives us into each of her characters, who was the guilty party in, say, "The Mystery of the Golden Thimble," or "Who wrote the Rhyming Charade?" How clear it is that in an Elizabeth or a Jane (this latter either Bennet or Fairfax), or an Anne Eliot, could never have purloined a thimble (though Elizabeth might indeed have mislaid it). But those giddy girls, Lydia and Kitty, might have borrowed one without permission, and Lady Catherine might have impounded a gold thimble without condescending to explanation, feeling it to be above Charlotte's station. . . .

There could be circumstances in which any

of these might—(of course, only temporarily) —have purloined a thimble. Similarly, we know that neither Mr. Collins nor Mr. Darcy, though for very different reasons, would have been capable of writing a charade, whereas Mr. Wickham or Mr. Bingley might easily have done so.

It is the essence of a good detective story that no one should do anything out of his character. How supreme, then, would Jane Austen have been in this field! The discovery of the criminal in such cases as these would be a sure following of a fine thread through a labyrinth, clear and temperate as a series of conservatories.

But deduction of the purely objective sort is a different affair, and in a book of this character it is obviously only the objective signs, and of those only the essentials, which can be told. We are reduced to the mechanics, or, if you prefer the more swagger term, to the mathematics, of detection. The game is stark and simple, but such as it is, is a good game, and these authors observe the most important rule of it—they play fairly.

Personally, I made rather a poor show when at a Baffle Party, but I did work out successfully the case of "The Murdered Physician," and I can assure the reader that there is no cosier sensation than the self-congratulation felt on solving one of the problems. Other people may make lucky guesses, but you yourself have worked out the thing intelligently and have deserved to be right.

F. TENNYSON JESSE.

FOR ALL WHO REVEL IN
CRIME DETECTION

How often you have been week-ending at the Duchess's place only to hear the butler break in on the festive company with the tragic announcement that the master has been found slain in the billiard-room, an Oriental dagger driven through his breast? And, fastened to the hilt by ribbon obviously from a wedding-cake box, a note — heliotrope-scented — on which is scrawled: " At last!" But the murderer has not signed it, and no one recognizes the handwriting. And there you are—everyone flabbergasted and in utter confusion. No one, not even the Big Four, can make anything out of the clues, so the whole company, including yourself, is suspected of the crime.

A nice pickle to be in! And why? Simply because you never developed your latent powers of observation and deduction—those qualities of mind which make the solution of the most inscrutable mysteries a veritable pleasure. Confess it, you never heeded Conan

Doyle; you thought it was all tosh. But it isn't, as this book will show.

A NEW AND CHALLENGING SPORT

The Baffle Book, with its mysteries and detective problems to be solved from given data and clues, will soon convert you to the enormous importance of observation and deduction. Solve a few dozen of the hypothetical crime mysteries that follow and you will be equipped to work out any given crime at any given house-party at any given moment.

"What do you deduce?" will be the question on everyone's lips as soon as the Baffle Book reaches the public. Here are the evidences of the crime. These are the facts established by the police. What do you observe? Which are the tell-tale clues? What do you deduce? How will you answer the questions asked of you at the end of each mystery problem: " Who is guilty?" or "What motive?" etc. As you use your reasoning powers in the solution of each problem, so you will be rated according to the credits specified in the book. And if you are really baffled, then you can look up the true solution in the Answer Section in the back of the book. (To consult this, shut the book, turn it upside down and open the book again as usual. The answers are printed upside down to deter you from looking too quickly for the solutions of the mysteries. It is more fun to work them out for yourself first.)

YOU WILL BE BAFFLED

Most of the mysteries are not easy to solve at first glance. That is what makes them interesting. But each has a logical and absolute solution which can be deduced reasonably by any intelligent and well-informed person. You must consider all the circumstances of the crime or mystery as stated in the text or as given in the chart or diagram or illustration, if one accompanies the problem. Any, or all together, may yield the clue or clues essential for the unravelling of the mystery. Observe, deduce, reason it out. Don't guess or jump to conclusions; you will probably be wrong.

THE BAFFLE BOOK KEEPS FAITH

The mysteries propounded here are not trick puzzles or riddles with far-fetched answers to

be guessed at. There are no trivial " catches "
to mislead you. When the book says: " The
police established the following as a fact "—
the reader may accept that as a fact. The clues
to the solution of the mystery are always there ;
it is for the reader to see them in their significance and to deduce from them in the light of
the general situation.

In other words, the Baffle Book—unlike
many detective stories—keeps faith with the
reader by disclosing all the evidence that exists.
It does not withhold vital facts for the purpose
of baffling you. If the book asks: " Was it the
butler or the chauffeur who committed the
crime?" you may assume that one or the other
of them did, and you will not find the Answer
Section lugging in the hitherto unsuspected
ashman as the culprit.

THE IMPORTANCE OF THE
SMALL CLUE

The seemingly trifling and insignificant clue
may be the most revealing of all, and this is as
it should be, for the annals of crime are filled
with cases in which brilliant reasoning from
faint clues has led to the solution of the
mystery.

What could be more admirable than the celebrated feat of M. Goron, Prefect of Police in Paris forty years ago? A wealthy widow was reported missing from her home in the French capital, and foul play was suspected. She had disappeared one afternoon en route to a friend's house where she had promised to spend the night. She had never arrived at her destination. No trace of her could be found. Her nephews were suspected and shadowed. It looked very bad for her favourite nephew, for he stood to profit handsomely by her death.

Several months later a woman's body was found in a Paris park. Such was the condition of the corpse and clothing that not even the widow's servants could say definitely whether it was or was not the body of the widow. The servants ventured that it was, but the nephews said not. The mystery deepened.

Then M. Goron noticed that one of the nephews seemed less perturbed than might have been expected. The famous detective examined again the room of the missing widow and in a drawer found a soiled lace collar with a tiny brown spot on the back. The collar belonged to the widow, and the spot proved to be not blood, but hair dye. It had been overlooked at first.

" So, then, your mistress dyed her hair, did she?" M. Goron said to a servant. " And how long had she been doing this?"

" She began about three months before she disappeared," was the reply.

M. Goron again examined the room and took inventory. He found no bottle of hair dye. All other possessions of the widow, except a nightgown, tooth-brush, hair-brush and comb, were found in their proper places. The widow had gone, she said, to spend but one night at her friend's—and had never arrived.

" Why should she have taken the hair dye with her for merely an overnight visit?" M. Goron asked himself. She would not have done so, he thought. But she did take it, he reasoned back, and it was precious and essential to her. He deduced that she knew that she would be away longer than she had said.

Why would a rich widow secretly flee with hair dye? For a lover, and a young one, reasoned M. Goron. And he solved the case thereby, for the detective also reasoned that she must have a confidante in one of her nephews, and both were watched. The one upon whom suspicion of murder of his aunt had rested more heavily was caught mailing to her in London a fresh supply of the very same hair dye! It was essential to the widow's appearance in the eyes of the young Frenchman with whom she had fled four months before. The widow had wished to deceive everyone. The corpse was later identified as that of an Italian spy.

That was observation and reasoning triumphant!

Watch for similar subtleties in some of the mysteries to follow. *En garde!* Twenty-eight crimes have been committed awaiting your solution. What do you deduce?

HOW TO GIVE A BAFFLE PARTY

The Baffle Book grew out of a game. It lends itself well to use at any gathering or party. As devised by two mystery story writers to amuse studio gatherings in New York last winter, the game is sometimes called "Clues" or Baffling Mysteries." So popular were these concocted mysteries with the players who tracked down the clues, that the best of the problems propounded have been put into book form by the originators. Now anyone can play merely with the aid of this book.

PLAYING SIDES

(Requiring two Baffle Books)

The host and hostess, or detective captains appointed by them, divide the group into two squads by choosing sides. Each team, armed with a Baffle Book, retires to an end of the room. At a given signal each begins work, simultaneously, on a certain mystery problem agreed upon. The team first solving a mystery announces it, without, of course, looking in the Answer Section. If right, the team gets all the credit specified in the book for answering the questions and a bonus of 10 besides (for speed). But if wrong, the team gets no credit and is penalised 5 for jumping to hasty conclusions. In short, the Baffle Book sets a premium on reasoning rather than guessing.

THE ONE-BOOK GAME

It is easy to amuse and baffle your friends by reading a problem to them aloud, slowly and distinctly. Give each player a pencil and paper in case he wants to take a note or two (although this is not necessary); but don't let anyone ask a question until you are through reading the data as given.

For purposes of a game a certain time is allotted for the solution of a problem—make it two or three or five minutes, as you prefer. Of course if everyone is baffled at the end of the first reading, you may re-read the problem or parts of it—but only by unanimous consent of those playing. At the end of the allotted time you call a halt and read the solution from the Answer Section. Those who have been baffled and have written nothing down correctly score nothing. Those partly solving get credit for what they have done. Whoever gets the highest total score of the evening wins the title of Sherlock Holmes and is automatically licensed to carry a magnifying glass.

Naturally it always helps a Baffle Party if the host serves shag tobacco. Give a Baffle Party.

P. S.—It is considered the depth of infamy to spread the solutions to the mysteries around the office or neighbourhood. Baffle someone with them first.

HINTS FOR SOLVING

Read the text of the mystery or detective problem carefully and consider the questions **you are asked** at the end of it.

If a diagram of the crime scene, or an illustration of any kind, accompanies the text of the mystery, examine that also for clues; it may give you a clue all by itself or it may tell you something which will further explain a clue in the text.

Sufficient clues from which the answers can be deduced are always to be found in the data given. Observe, deduce, reason out the solution—don't guess or jump to conclusions.

Don't admit you are baffled until you have spent at least five minutes on the shorter problems, or fifteen minutes apiece on the longer mysteries.

Even when you are baffled, try to answer some of the questions at the end of the problem before you look up the solution in the Answer Section.

To find the Answer Section, shut the book, turn it upside down, and open again as usual; i.e., the Answer Section is printed upside-down.

For each question rightly answered, you gain certain credits. Mark these down as you go along, under " Credit Score."

WHO MURDERED ELLINGTON BREESE?

Suspicion of guilt of the murder is narrowed down to two men. Which of them committed the crime and how do you know it? Examine carefully the following established facts, then answer the questions put at the end of the problem.

London was shocked on the morning of June 5, 1925, by the news of the murder of a distinguished citizen. Ellington Breese, founder and president of the Breese Chemical Works, near Gravesend, had been murdered by poison gas generated in his bedroom during the night.

Breese was a good deal of a " character," and insisted on living not far from his works, in what had been a Victorian gentleman's country house near the river. It was now approached on the landward side by villas, though marsh-land, intersected by dykes, still stretched towards the river.

The police investigation revealed the following pertinent facts:

Breese had been found dead in his bed at eight o'clock in the morning by his servant, who for years had aroused him at that hour. On the mantelpiece (there was no fireplace) the police found a glass flask of about one quart capacity. Its stopper was missing. It was the kind of glass vessel familiar to any chemical laboratory. Experts said that one chemical poured upon another would have generated the poison gas immediately, and that diffusion in the room must have followed quickly. Neither on the glass flask nor on other objects were fingerprints found.

Although both windows had been up eight inches from the bottom, the practically instantaneous effects of the gas had killed every living thing in the bedroom. Breese's pet bullfinch lay dead in its cage. Half a dozen flies lay dead on the window sills. It was exceptionally hot weather and the flies had been troublesome. The dark green blinds at the windows were found drawn down nearly to the bottom of the lower window sash, dimming the murder chamber, though the sun shone brightly outside.

The wavering finger of suspicion began to

point with equal emphasis at two young men, each of whom was connected with Ellington Breese's business and had had enough laboratory experience to have manufactured the deadly gas.

Breese Walters, nephew and only surviving relative of the murdered man, was one suspect. Adam Boardman, Breese's confidential secretary, was the other. Each protested his innocence, each to a degree had an alibi. According to the police investigation, so far as could be determined, both had good records, no debts or entanglements. Both seemed deeply affected by the tragedy.

Neither man seemed capable of committing such a cowardly crime. Yet the police reflected upon the terms of Breese's will, which divided half his estate—about one hundred thousand pounds—between the favourite nephew and the devoted employée. The other half of the estate Breese had bequeathed to charity. The terms of the will, drawn five years before, had never been a secret.

Walters and Boardman had maintained cordial but not close relations while in the employ of Breese. Each expressed confidence in the innocence of the other.

The coroner examined the body at 9.30 a.m.

and declared that Breese had been dead at least four hours, and possibly for as long as ten hours. The position of the body in the bed indicated to a certainty that death had overtaken Breese while in his bed, to which he had been confined by a slight illness. The police, cherishing a uniform suspicion of Walters and Boardman, decided that they would know the murderer when they knew approximately the hour in which the poison gas was generated in Breese's bedroom.

Boardman, the secretary, had been with Breese until a little after 11.30 p.m. He admitted it, and his leaving the house about a quarter to twelve was confirmed by the testimony of old Mrs. Grew, Breese's boyhood nurse and housekeeper, whose room was near Breese's on the second floor. Boardman had been discussing business matters with his employer, who was laid up in bed convalescing from influenza. He admitted returning to Breese's bedroom for a moment after first leaving it, in order, he said, to secure a briefcase which he had forgotten. At that time, he said, he put out the bedroom light at Breese's request, and closed the door upon leaving. And after leaving Breese's home Boardman went in his little two-seater car, straight to the

Dormy House of a local golf club, where he lived. Through the rest of the night and until the body was found his alibi was perfect.

Walters had been in Manchester all day. He got back to London in time for a late supper at his club, and arrived at the house near Gravesend at one o'clock in the morning. Mrs. Grew heard him enter, came out and spoke to him on the second floor landing and asked if there was anything she might do. Walters said he was not hungry and would go straight to bed. He asked about his uncle's health, heard that Boardman had been there until nearly midnight attending to details of business, and observed that his uncle must be recovering nicely from his influenza if he could remain at work so late. He went upstairs to his room on the third floor.

Mrs. Grew, who was suffering from rheumatism, returned to her room on the second floor, read for a while, and then went to sleep —not until 2.30 a.m., she believed. From that time until the discovery of the murder, Walters's claim of innocence, like Boardman's, had no support from other testimony than his own.

In short, the police suspected, and their suspicions proved well founded, that if Breese died before midnight it was Boardman who liberated the gas that killed him; and that if Breese died after midnight, then Walters was the slayer of his uncle.

You have now all the evidence from which Scotland Yard shrewdly fixed the approximate time of the crime and thereby the identity of the murderer.

These are the questions for you to answer:

1. *Which was the slayer?* (Credit 5.)

2. *How did the police deduce it?* (Credit 5.)

Credit Score:

NOTE

When you have answered the questions, turn to page 1 of the Answer Section for the solution, and rate yourself accordingly. The sense or gist of your answers, not the exact phrasing, determines whether or not you have answered rightly.

Rate yourself in the line above marked "Credit Score."

THE EVIDENCE ON THE JAPANNED BOX

The theft of the celebrated Elgin Emerald occurred under circumstances most embarrassing to Mr. Stephen Lerian, owner of the unique gem. Lerian had been entertaining a house party at his place in Hampshire. The guests were five in number:

Mr. and Mrs. Archibald Hay; their niece, Charlotte Grainger; Colonel Alexander Blue; and Mrs. Eleanor Standish, widow of one of Lerian's old college friends.

With what he himself later characterised as inexcusable carelessness, Lerian, the host, had left the emerald in a small black japanned box upon a table in the living room, after exhibiting it to the assembled guests one evening. He had been trying for some time to get through a telephone call to London, and when finally summoned to the telephone in an adjacent room, absent-mindedly laid the box on the table and hurried out. When he returned in five minutes, the box was empty.

Assuming that the party was playing a joke on him Lerian, in mock-serious tones, demanded that the thief step forward. For several minutes he could hardly believe his senses when each of the company, with the utmost emphasis, denied any knowledge of the missing jewel. Judson, the butler, had been in the room during Lerian's absence, as had Ada Gowan, a maid, but these old servants of good character, also denied all knowledge of the matter.

For two hours the entire household was in the throes of an excited search on the theory that the jewel had been accidentally lost. But at last Lerian was compelled to face the truth: *someone had taken it*.

To call in the police on so obviously an " inside job " was revolting to Lerian's nature. Absolving everyone from blame in the matter except himself, and insisting that he must have spilled it from the box, he forbade further discussion of the subject, and with remarkable *sang-froid* swept his guests into a game of bridge. It would " turn up," said Lerian.

Afterwards, in his own room, with the japanned box before him, Lerian, who is something of an amateur detective, examined the box carefully.

Its surface was highly polished. On the outer rim of the inside of the cover he discovered a remarkably clear thumbprint, which he believed was not his own. He sprinkled it with the white powder used to bring out fingerprints on black surfaces and found it another's. Then he set the box carefully aside.

Lerian knew that none of the company had laid hands on the inside when he had first shown it to them. He reasoned (and subsequent events justified his reasoning) that this must be the thumbprint of the thief. But whose thumbprint? The innocent ones must not suffer suspicion. He resorted to a stratagem.

Lerian put the japanned box carefully away in a wall safe. He then took from his Oriental collection a nest of small black lacquered boxes, whose surfaces were even more tell-tale than the jewel case. The following morning, Lerian contrived to exhibit to each guest and each servant a different one of the lacquered boxes. To each person separately he told an attractive story of the history of the box and got each to test the strength of the apparently fragile sides by squeezing them between finger and thumb of the left hand; for the thief's thumbprint, as placed on the cover of the case, indicated that a left hand had made it.

Each box, bearing a different thumbmark, Lerian duly secreted in his bureau. When this was done he withdrew to his room and treated the seven small lacquered boxes with white powder. Each, of course, he had subsequently labelled for purposes of identification.

On the next page is a reproduction of the thumbprint on the lid of the japanned jewel case, and the thumbprints on the seven lacquered boxes.

What do you deduce? The questions to be answered are:

1. *Did a guest or a servant steal Stephen Lerian's emerald?* (Credit 5.)

2. *Who was the thief?* (Credit 5.)

Credit Score:

FINGERPRINT OF THE THIEF

ON THE JAPANNED BOX

MRS. HAY'S

MR. HAY'S

JUDSON'S

COL. BLUE'S

MRS. STANDISH'S

MISS GRAINGER'S

ADA GOWAN'S

THE ELEVATED TRANSIT MYSTERY

This is a three-part mystery. Solve the first part before trying the second, and both before the third—or you will be baffled indeed.

PART I

While sitting at the window of Cho Sing's Chop Suey Restaurant, at the corner of Tenth Avenue and Forty-eighth Street, early Sunday morning, July 7th, Arthur McGraw and Queenie Walker witnessed the beginning of the celebrated mystery which for eleven days was the sensation of the country. Cho Sing's restaurant occupies the third floor of the building. The table at the window, where the couple sat, is some seven feet below the level of the tracks of the Tenth Avenue Line of the Elevated Transit Company. As all the world knows, and as the accompanying illustration makes clear, the elevated railway—colloquially known as " the L "—is the overhead means of transit in New York City. The trains run on a permanent way laid on high steel trestles.

As McGraw subsequently testified (corroborated by Miss Walker) they had been watching anxiously to see if the rain were stopping, so that they might leave. Several times during the previous half hour they had been fascinated by the oncoming roar and rush of the elevated trains, which bore down upon them only to swerve sharply to the left not more than fifteen feet from their window and grind around the curve which marks the turn of the line from Tenth Avenue onto Forty-eighth Street.

At approximately 2.28 a.m. they had just noticed that the shower had stopped and were watching the last car of a train swing around the curve, when they were startled to see the figure of a man hurtle downwards close to the edge of the elevated road and fall on the pavement below. McGraw summoned Cho Sing and several men at neighbouring tables and rushed downstairs to render aid.

What they found was even more shocking than they had expected. The man had fallen on his side and had rolled over and over onto a dry spot on the pavement which had been protected by an awning. He lay prone, and on turning the man over, the would-be rescuers gasped to find a crimson stain which nearly covered the white starched bosom of his evening-dress shirt. He was dead. Indeed, it was apparent that the man had been dead from stabs even before he struck the pavement.

His face was that of a man in his early thirties—dark, handsome, evidently of foreign extraction.

Policeman O'Connor, arriving on the scene at 2.33, immediately isolated the body of the man from the gathering crowd and telephoned headquarters at 2.34. Police headquarters telephoned the news to the Elevated Transit Company officials and ordered the train to be stopped at the nearest station as quickly as it could be done. The records establish that the train was stopped and held at the Forty-second Street Station on Eighth Avenue at 2.36, pending the arrival of detectives.

Several detectives from the Forty-fourth Street police station arrived a few minutes later and made a detailed examination of all guards and passengers on the train. The following facts were established:

There was unanimous testimony that no man in evening dress had ridden in the train since it started from One Hundred and Eightieth Street. William Murphy, transit guard in charge of the platforms connecting the last and middle cars of the train (it was a three-

Where the Tenth Avenue line of the Elevated Transit turns left on to Forty-eighth Street. Long arrow at right indicates window where McGraw and Queenie sat. X marks spot where body struck pavement

car train), denied that there could have been a stabbing affray on the platform or within either of his cars. He was corroborated by seven reputable witnesses. No testimony gathered revealed any knowledge of the presence of a man answering the description of the dead man. The detectives were baffled.

But since McGraw and Miss Walker, the witnesses of the fall, were certain that they had seen the man fall from the last car, the detectives held Guard Murphy for examination, took the addresses of all fourteen passengers in the rear car, and had the train switched and held. They also picked up " White " Mizzinski, wanted for arson in connection with the Brooklyn apartment house fires. " White " denied any knowledge of the dead man, and his entrance to the train at the Fifty-fourth Street Station, was substantiated.

The detectives then returned to the scene at Cho Sing's and re-examined the body. They established the following additional details:

Height, 5 feet 6 inches; approximate weight, 140 pounds; cheap quality of cloth in evening clothes. Label of the maker had been cut from clothes. All marks on linen had been removed. No cuff links, wallet, paper, money, or watch were found upon the body.

The patent leather shoes on the victim's feet, soles of which first appeared wet with patches of water, upon careful examination proved to have been waxed. The rain, which had thoroughly soaked the back of the coat and of the trousers, the back of the socks, and even the hair on the back of the head, had been warded off the soles of the shoes. The soles were slippery, but not wet. The front of the victim's clothes was dry.

The man had been stabbed twice in the heart, apparently with a long, sharp knife. No finger-prints could be found.

Police Captain Danforth, who arrived at Cho Sing's place soon after the fall of the body, had already established from the testimony of a section track walker (who had inspected the tracks only eight minutes before the tragedy) that the body probably could not have been on the tracks before the arrival of the train, which passed the curve at 2.28 a.m.

As is now well known, Captain Danforth, by reasoning solely from the evidence up to then available, reached certain conclusions which were of the greatest importance in the ultimate solution of the mystery. Especially he deduced correctly how the body had come to the pavement and what should be done at once.

What do you deduce?   These are the questions to be answered:

1. *How came the body to be upon the pavement?*   (Credit 4.)

2. *Where should the detectives particularly search for clues which might ultimately lead to the catching of the murderer?*   (Credit 1.)

Credit Score:

Part II

Have you read and solved the preceding problem—Part I of " The Elevated Transit Mystery"?   It is essential to an understanding of the part which follows.

It is a tribute to Captain Danforth's detective ability in seeking the solution of the Elevated Transit mystery that he called immediately upon the United States Government's local Weather Bureau for data to help him. The body had been seen to fall at approximately 2.28 a.m., and within forty minutes the captain had obtained an official bureau report of the duration of the rainfall in the uptown district where the tragedy had been discovered. The report showed that the shower had burst suddenly at 2.20 a.m. and had continued for seven minutes, then stopping. At no time had the rain been merely a drizzle. And there had been no rain in the city for nineteen hours previous to that time.

With this established fact before him Captain Danforth would be in a position to consider other facts which he had obtained. First, a map of the Elevated Transit Company's Tenth Avenue line, showing the various stations uptown (i.e., above Cho Sing's restaurant) and a schedule of Train No. 34 (from which the body had fallen) from its point of origin down to the Forty-eighth Street region. The train, he had ascertained, had been on time all the way down. Captain Danforth had also ordered that the map be marked to show at which points the tracks of the elevated railroad *ran nearest to* the buildings and apartment houses along the seven-mile route. These " zones of suspicion " were three in number. They are indicated by dotted rings on the map which is reproduced on page 31.

Most important of all, Captain Danforth had made a personal examination of the roof of the rear-end car of Train No 34 immediately after he had deduced that the body probably had fallen from there. The evidence clearly confirmed his conclusion. On the still moist roof, near the very rear of the car, was a dry spot roughly shaped like a cross. Obviously it had been made by the sprawled body of a man whose arms had been extended on either side. It was apparent also that he had lain face down, for a patch of blood stained the dry spot just above the centre of it. The victim, it will be recalled, had been stabbed in the heart.

Now the most obvious place from which a body could have been thrown conveniently to a train passing below was the bridge at the One Hundred and Twentieth Street station uptown. This bridge connects the uptown with the downtown stations at that point. Captain Danforth had therefore dispatched detectives to that station very early in his investigation. Their report, when telephoned to him, proved to be of the greatest importance in connection with the data which he had assembled.

The detectives had found an important witness in the person of Inspector Monahan of the Elevated Transit Company. His night inspection tours (of the signal light system recently installed) customarily brought him to the One Hundred and Twentieth Street station about

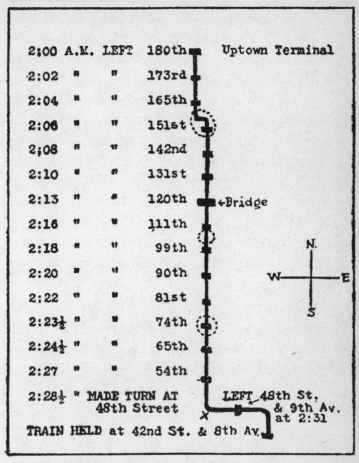

2:00 A.M. LEFT 180th   Uptown Terminal

2:02 " " 173rd

2:04 " " 165th

2:06 " " 151st

2:08 " " 142nd

2:10 " " 131st

2:13 " " 120th ←Bridge

2:16 " " 111th

2:18 " " 99th

2:20 " " 90th

2:22 " " 81st

2:23½ " " 74th

2:24½ " " 65th

2:27 " " 54th

2:28½ " MADE TURN AT   LEFT 48th St.
      48th Street   & 9th Av.
                       at 2:31
X

TRAIN HELD at 42nd St. & 8th Av.

Map of the elevated line. "Zones of Suspicion" are shown by
dotted rings. X marks where body was seen to fall

2.10 o'clock.   Monahan said that he had been
smoking a pipe on the bridge while waiting for
Train 106 (bound uptown and then not due for
eight minutes) when he observed Train 34
come from uptown, stop at the One Hundred
and Twentieth Street Station, and pass on
downtown. He was absolutely certain that the
body could not have been on the roof of the
train at that time, else he would have observed
it. The police found his testimony convincing,
and indeed it may be said that his testimony
was confirmed by later discoveries.

Where should further clues be sought? This
was the question confronting Captain Danforth at this stage of the investigation. He proceeded to narrow down the three "zones of
suspicion" to one in which the murderer must
have operated. What conclusion would you
have reached from the available data?

The question to be answered is:

*To which "zone of suspicion" did Captain
Danforth direct the search for further clues to
the murderer?*   (Credit 2.)

Credit Score:

PART III

Have you read and solved the preceding parts of this mystery? Parts I and II should be done before the following third and final part is attempted.

Under Captain Danforth's directions detectives combed the " zone of suspicion " where it seemed most probable that further clues might be found. The Tenth Avenue line of the Elevated Transit Company in this region ran through a section of the city quite mixed in population and in style of buildings. For eight blocks the dingy avenue squeezed itself into a small canyon scarcely thirty-five feet wide in some parts. Drab tenement houses four and five storeys high lined the elevated tracks for much of this distance. A hay-and-feed stores loft, remnant of the days of the horse; several pool parlours ; a Rumanian restaurant (on a third floor) ; and the " Rooms of the One Hundred and Fifth Social Club " (on a fourth floor) were conspicuous among the non-residential apartments on the east side of the avenue.

On the west side of the avenue, besides private dwelling apartments in tenement houses, were to be seen the dinghy offices of a Russian newspaper; the gaudy, glaring windows of the Palace Gardens, a dance hall; the Calliope Saxophone School; a storage warehouse seven storeys high; and several disreputable-looking armchair lunches and cafetarias. All but the latter had windows which opened *above* the level of the roofs of the elevated train cars as they passed.

With the exception of the newspaper office, the hay-and-feed store, and the storage warehouse, all the non-residential apartments enumerated had been open late that evening. It was obvious that, once located, the building from which the body had been thrown would have to be searched carefully. One place in particular, Captain Danforth decided, was most suspicious of all. He decided on this place by considering certain facts noted in the early stage of the investigation.

In this place his men found clues which led, some ten days later, to discovery and capture of the murderer. Where would you have searched especially?

The questions to be answered are:

1. *In which building did Captain Danforth's men find clues which ultimately led to the detection of the murderer of the victim whose*

body was thrown upon the roof of Train 34?
(Credit 2.)

2. How did Captain Danforth deduce that
this building rather than any other was worth
special investigation?   (Credit 1.)

Credit Score:
  Part I:
  Part II:
  Part III:

THE PROBLEM OF THE FORGER'S TORN NOTE

This is a simple problem which will serve to prepare for more complicated mysteries to come.

Early in the evening of August 4, 1927, Scotland Yard received a tip through the underworld that "Red" Sam Gunther, long suspected as the leader of a band of high-class forgers, could be found in the vicinity of a deserted warehouse on a wharf at Limehouse. The informer's story proved to be correct; Gunther was surrounded by plain-clothes police and was fatally shot after he had opened fire on his captors.

When surprised, Gunther had just drawn a scrap of paper from his pocket and was in the act of reading it. At the first demand for surrender from the cordon closing in on him, Gunther was seen to jump back, tear the note in fragments and thrust them in his mouth as

he drew his automatic pistol. Two detectives
fired and the criminal collapsed, but not before
he had managed to destroy parts of the paper.
All but two fragments were chewed beyond
legibility. These are shown here. The detectives reconstructed them in order to ascertain
the message which Gunther had deemed so important.

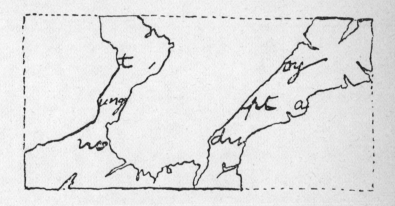

From these fragments Scotland Yard was
able to deduce the time and place of what
proved to be a meeting of the gang. Gunther's
death was kept secret, and the police were
present at the *rendezvous* with startling suc-
cess.

Had you been there as a detective, what
would you have deduced?

The questions to be answered are:

1. *Where did the gang plan to meet?* (Credit 5.)

2. *When?* (Credit 5.)

Credit Score:

THE SANDY PENINSULA FOOT-PRINT MYSTERY

No witnesses to the Sandy Peninsula tragedy were available, but the detectives on the case were able to deduce substantially all that had happened on the lonely beach that bright June afternoon. Footprints told the story. What do they tell you? In this problem the diagram should be studied carefully.

On the South Coast of England there is a sandy peninsula not yet invaded by the speculative builder who has covered the coast some five miles away with a mass of red bungalows. Through the centre of the peninsula runs a macadamised road, made while the builder was still optimistic, it is skirted on each side by a scrubby hedge of bushes which thrive in slender margins of soil filled in at the time of the building of the road. The road ends at the east in the sea wall. Toward the west it runs with many twistings to the bungalow town, five miles away by land.

At five o'clock in the afternoon on the 2nd day of June, Walter Derring, a tourist, unaware that the road led nowhere, was motoring along it from the west, and stopped his car not far from the peninsula end of the road to examine something which had caught his eye through the bushes. It proved to be the dead body of a man with an ugly bruise on the chin. Derring saw footprints in the sand around the body and immediately comprehended the necessity of an official police investigation before the trails might be confused by footprints of the curious public. He raced his car back to the nearest A.A. telephone box, two miles away, where the peninsula road joined the main road, and fetched police to the spot within twenty minutes.

One of the policemen immediately recognised the dead man as Revington Strang, a retired London business man, reputed to be rich, but eccentric, and lately (since separation from his wife) almost a recluse. He had been living in an old manor house on the downs behind the bungalow town for several months. An inveterate horseman, his grim figure had frequently been observed of late on the sands and bypaths of the peninsula.

Strang's reputation as a tyrannical and

headstrong character had been long since established in city circles, and it had been no surprise to London society circles when his wife,
the former Dorothy Wilfred, left him soon after
the marriage. To Strang's few friends it was
no secret that this had cut him deeply. He had
predicted more than once that she would return
to him.

The police first examined carefully the beach
of the peninsula (see the two-page diagram
herewith). It had rained most of the morning,
and the damp sand showed clear footprint
trails. The chief constable of the county, who
was at once sent for, soon found that Strang's
wife had been staying at the Golf Hotel in the
bungalow town for several weeks, but had been
out since noon and had not returned. They
also learned from a lighthouse keeper five miles
away, that a man and a woman had been seen
to land on the south-west corner of the peninsula in a canoe " about three o'clock " that
afternoon. The keeper, happening to observe
them through his binocular glass, could testify
to nothing more than that. He had not
watched them and had not observed whether
or not they departed.

The detectives further established that low
tide at the peninsula that afternoon was at

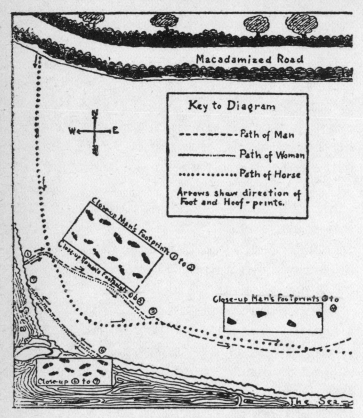

Macadamized Road

Key to Diagram

- - - - - - Path of Man
————— Path of Woman
.... Path of Horse

Arrows show direction of
Foot and Hoof-prints.

Close-up Man's Footprints ① to ②

Close-up Woman's Footprints ③ to ④

Close-up Man's Footprints ⑤ to ⑥

Close-up ⑥ to ⑦

The Sea

Scene of the Sandy Peninsula Tragedy as it

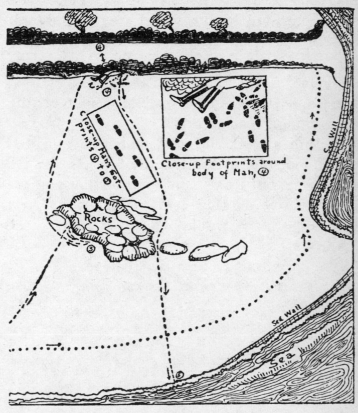

Close-up Mans Foot-
prints ④ to ⑤

Close-up Footprints around
body of Man, ④

Rocks

Sea Wall

Sea Wall

Sea

appeared to the detectives at 5.30 p.m., June 2nd.

2.40, and that Strang had left his house for a ride about 1.30 that afternoon. Finally they established that Mrs. Strang had been seen almost constantly during her stay at the Golf Hotel in the company of a wealthy American. Of him they could learn nothing for the moment, except that he was reputed young, handsome, and a former welterweight boxing champion at Yale.

Within a week the newspapers had printed the full details of the tragedy and its strange aftermath, but let us now suppose that you are the detective on the scene. What would you deduce? How would you reconstruct the tragedy?

The questions to be answered are:

1. *What happened at the spot marked 2 on the diagram?* (Credit 1.)

2. *What did man do between 2 and 3?* (Credit 1.)

3. *What did man do at 3?* (Credit 1.)

4. *What happened on road near 4?* (Credit 1.)

5. *What became of woman after 4?* (Credit 1.)

6. *What happened near 5?* (Credit 1.)

7. *What happened between 5 and 6?* (Credit 1.)

8. *What happened between 6 and 7?* (Credit 1.)

9. *What happened after 7?* (Credit 1.)

10. *Where, in all probability, did the horse go after the event at 4?* (Credit 1.)

Credit Score:

No. 6

THE CASE OF THE STOLEN VAN DYCK

Can you recognise handwriting through its disguise? Here is an interesting problem in detection.

The Portrait of an Officer, Van Dyke's celebrated painting, since 1907, has been the star of the small but select group of Old Masters in the collection of the Farjeon Memorial Museum of one of the big northern manufacturing towns. On the morning of May 4, 1926, this picture was missing. It had been stolen after the museum was closed to the public (at 5.30) on the afternoon of the 3rd. It had been crudely hacked out of its frame, which was left hanging.

The police investigation conducted by Detective-Inspector Arthur Hurst could develop no evidences of burglary, nor of the crime having been committed by expert cracksmen or professional thieves. At doors, windows, and skylights Hurst found no signs of forcible entry. Obviously it was one more " inside job."

At once suspicion focused upon three men having more or less independent access to the museum building. The three were:

JOHN GREGG, night watchman, fifty-six years old, married—who customarily came on duty at 6 p.m., but who on the evening of May 3rd happened to be twenty-one minutes late in reporting.

HARRY SIMS, the day attendant, thirty-nine years old, unmarried—whose duty it was to wait and turn over his keys to Gregg, receiving them again from the watchman at 8.30 a.m. the next day.

JAMES WEAVER, engineer and repair man, forty-nine years old, married, but recently become a widower, who virtually had access to the museum building at all hours, and who had been on duty there on May 3rd as late as 7 p.m., since the weather was raw and the steam-heating plant demanded his attention.

Each denied any knowledge of the theft. The curator, Frederick Jones, was deemed above suspicion.

To recover the Dutch
painting obey strickly.
I mean it.

Sample of handwriting of the ransom note

I used to get $75. a month at
the department store but I would

Sample of handwriting of James Weaver

I used to be the watchman at McDougall's Dept. Store and I

Sample of handwriting of John Gregg

Sample of handwriting of Harry Sims

49

The Farjeon Collection contained other
treasures, but the Van Dyck was its richest
prize, so famous the world over, it could not
be sold by a thief; and the trustees of the
museum considered offering a " no questions
asked " reward.   But this the police vetoed.
Detective Hurst said he might be able to trap
the guilty one among the three suspects and
force him to confess his crime.

But at noon the chairman of the museum's
trustees received an astonishing note in a plain
envelope, bearing a local postmark, of that day.
It was in a handwriting obviously disguised:

*To recover the Dutch painting obey strictly.
Price is £5,000 cash, otherwise will be
destroyed. I mean it. Tell someone to take the
10.22 train to-morrow morning for London.
Tell him to tip the guard to keep the last first-
class compartment free for him. When you see
a man beside track waving two small yellow
flags throw the money in a bag from the train.
The money has got to be in cash, in tens,
twenties, fifties and hundreds. Then the painting will be sent back all right. It will come by
express prepaid right away, but if the train
stops or any police interfere it will be hacked
up. I mean it. Maybe you will not see the man*

with the yellow flags soon after the train leaves and maybe not until near London. Watch sharp, and remember no tricks.

The trustees decided to take no chances of losing the painting and therefore secretly made preparations for carrying out the instructions of the ransom note. Only after the train had departed the following morning, bearing their representative in the rearmost first-class compartment with the money in a bag, was the ransom note revealed to Hurst. The handwriting interested him immensely. He immediately sought samples of the handwritings of the three suspects, and brief search in the records of the museum yielded enough to permit detailed comparison.

Portions of these are reproduced on another page. They were taken from letters applying for positions with the museum several years before the theft of the Van Dyck. A part of the ransom note is also shown.

The writing in the ransom note, the detective reasoned, might be the disguised writing of one of the suspects. Was it? If so, whose? Detective Hurst reached a decision after long study. and the trustees, who had taken due precautions to safeguard their ransom money, reached certain conclusions which checked with Detective Hurst's decision.

The question to be answered is:

Who wrote the ransom note about the stolen Van Dyck? (Credit 10.)

Credit Score:

THE WAYSIDE MYSTERY

Horace Twickenham, a farmer on the western outskirts of Southampton, arose at dawn one morning in August and, having attended to the stock, drove his cows down the road toward a pasture a quarter of a mile from the house. The road ran between fields bordered with bushes.

About two-thirds of the way down, a patch of bright red in the bushes at the south side of the road caught his eye, and on approaching he was appalled to discover the body of a young woman clothed in a flimsy silk dress of brilliant red. She had obviously been hurled into the wayside hedge, for whole bushes had been broken and flattened out by the impact of her body. A single glance at the unusually pretty face of the girl and at her bruised throat, told Twickenham that she had been strangled, and strangled by powerful hands. The victim was of medium height and of good figure.

Twickenham, recalling that one should not move the body of a person who might have been murdered (for fear of destroying valuable clues), immediately rushed to the house and telephoned to the nearest constabulary. The constable arrived in less than fifteen minutes, and with Twickenham he proceeded to note in detail the condition of the body and the bushes in the immediate neighbourhood.

The constable and Twickenham noted the following facts:

1. The body lay with head to the west and feet to the east. On the right foot was a high-heeled black patent leather slipper. The slipper from the left foot was missing. The light-coloured silk stockings were splashed by dew from the bushes. The red dress was also stained in patches a darker red from splashes of dew. The earth around, although soft, showed no footprints.

2. On the soft road one farm-cart track and the tracks of an automobile were distinctly visible. The automobile tracks swerved sharply from the centre of the road to the southern side of the road ten feet east from the point where the body lay, and swerved back to the centre of the road some five feet west of that spot.

Charging Twickenham to guard the body

and the surrounding scene, the constable rushed to the nearest telephone and gave the news to the Southampton police. Southampton was the nearest large town. The police agreed to send an expert medical officer and their detectives. Meanwhile they demanded information which might aid in apprehending the murderer, asking several pointed questions.

Fortunately, Constable Barge, although he had never had elaborate training in crime detection, possessed a remarkable native intelligence and was able to answer all of the questions with what proved to be substantial accuracy. Indeed, besides answering their questions, he displayed a bit of initiative in later seeking and finding an important piece of evidence. This eventually established the guilt of the murderer when he was later arrested upon suspicion by the Plymouth police at the request of the Scotland Yard authorities.

Considering the evidence available as described (and do not forget the police sketch), if you had had Constable Barge's responsibilities how would you have answered the questions of the Southampton police?

These are the questions to be answered:

1. *What brand of tyres did the car have?* (Credit 2.)

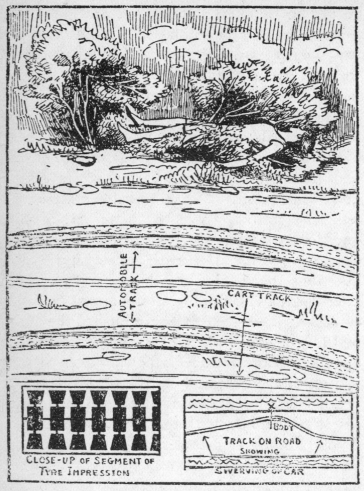

Sketch of scene near Twickenham's farm on outskirts of Southampton.
From photographs made by the police

2. *Was more than one man in the car?* (Credit 2.)

3. *Approximately how long had the body been there when discovered?* (Credit 2.)

4. *In which direction was the car travelling?* (Credit 2.)

5. *For what piece of evidence which might have afforded valuable clues would you have looked?* (Credit 1.)

6. *Where would you have looked for it?* (Credit 1.)

Credit Score:

THE DEATH THREAT CLUE

Late in October of last year the police succeeded in capturing a member of the so-called " 'Varsity Gang," which had been terrorising motorists in the Home Counties by hold-ups and car thefts. The prisoner, William Driscoll, aged 20, was committed for trial, and the approach of the trial excited unusual attention.

Ten days before the date set for it at the Assizes, Prosecuting Counsel began to receive threatening letters. The letters afforded no clues to the identity of the sender, but it was assumed that the author was the reputed leader of the gang, James Paget, a young man of good family, who had been sent down from Oxford in his second year because some mysterious thefts from fellow undergraduates were traced to him. He was not prosecuted, but he disappeared from the knowledge of his family, though the police had reason to believe he was the same man who had received a short sentence the following year, under the assumed name of James Brown, for stealing a motor-car.

Everyone who had been held up by the so-called " 'Varsity bandits " testified that the young man concerned spoke with what is sometimes unkindly called " the Oxford voice." Hence the popular nickname of the gang. Driscoll, as a matter of fact, was a Londoner, and had not been to a University. There was no doubt he belonged to the band of young men who had been infesting the Home Counties.

On the Friday before the Monday set for Driscoll's trial, Counsel for the Prosecution received a registered letter, of which the address was typewritten. Its postmark showed it to have been sent off from the south-west district of London, and what purported to be a return address was typed on the back of the envelope: " From Dies Irae, 76, Passmore Street, Stockwell, S.W." Within was a single sheet of white paper, on which had been pasted with ordinary gum, the following seventeen words:

if   you   go   on   with   the   trial   of   the   Prisoner

you   will   not   be   alive   on   SATURDAY

D. I.

The initials at the foot of the message were typewritten.

The police discovered that the Passmore Street address was a piece of grim humour, for it was the establishment of a well-known undertaker. So seriously did the police take the threat in the letter that a search was instituted for Paget, and the informers of the underworld were rigorously questioned. As a result Paget was found to be living under an assumed name in a small hotel chiefly used by sea-faring men at Greenwich.

Now, although it was a matter of common knowledge to the underworld and to the police that Paget during his many absences from his headquarters was the leader of the gang of car thieves, they had no proof sufficient to bring him to trial, and had not as yet any proof that it was he who sent the threatening letter. But as his record was so bad and he was a young man known to resort to violence, it was felt the safety of Counsel for the Prosecution might depend upon Paget's arrest.

He was shadowed from his rooms, which were then raided, and amongst the litter that covered the table—packs of cards, daily papers, an empty whisky bottle, and the like—they found conclusive evidence which positively fastened the guilt of the threatening letter upon Paget.

What would you have deducted from the letter? The question to be answered is:

What did the police find on the writing-table which conclusively fastened the guilt upon Paget? (Credit 10.)

THE SCULPTOR'S STUDIO MYSTERY

Which of the two suspects was guilty of the sculptor's murder? This was the baffling problem which confronted the police. What would you have deduced?

On the morning of November 3, 1922, Reginald Lamont, famous sculptor, was found dead in his studio in Bedford Park, London, W. His skull had been crushed in by several blows from his own sculptor's mallet, which was found not far from his body. The police were amazed to note that the head of a large clay statue of Juno in the centre of the studio had been smashed. Fragments of the head which lay on the floor had been so crushed that they must have been pounded with a mallet.

Suspicion immediately fastened upon two women. One was Lamont's wife, a dusky-haired Spanish-looking woman, thirty-seven years old, who was known to have posed for the statue of Juno, which Lamont had been com-

*Sketch from police photograph of Lamont's studio made soon after
the murder was discovered*

missioned to do for the garden of a well-known millionaire. The other suspect was a well-known model of Scandinavian origin, a statuesque creature who had already received considerable publicity in the cheaper illustrated papers when she had been cited as intervener in a notorious divorce suit.

This young woman of twenty-three years, Helga Halverson, was known to have been intimate with the sculptor of late, and admitted having posed for him, two weeks before, for a study of her head. This study was found in the studio.

In many ways it was one of the most baffling cases that had ever confronted Scotland Yard. Both women had seemingly airtight alibis for the afternoon during which the murder must have been committed. Indeed, each claimed not to have been in the studio for a week. Questioning of the suspects yielded no evidence conclusive of the guilt of either, and the officials were beginning to feel baffled, when a fresh detective called Coldstream entered the case.

Lamont's body had been discovered at 5 p.m. by James Hogan, elderly handy man who was accustomed to sweep the studio daily. The sculptor's well-appointed workshop (see sketch) and its adjoining living room were in a separate building two miles from his home on Chiswick Mall. According to Hogan's testimony, both living room and studio had been cleaned carefully at 12.30 p.m. in preparation for the sculptor's arrival to begin work soon after lunch. When questioned by Coldstream, Hogan testified specifically to having removed all ashes and dead embers from the large fireplace, swept it clean, and laid fresh tinder and logs. Hogan lighted the fire, as was his custom, when Lamont arrived at the studio.

According to Hogan, whose testimony was never shaken by the police, Lamont arrived at 1.10. He inquired for telephone messages and was told there had been none. The sculptor dismissed the handy man after a few minutes, requesting him to return at about five o'clock to clean up the studio after the day's work. Hogan returned at this time, discovered the body, and immediately telephoned the police. They instructed him to touch nothing and to lock the studio from the outside, pending the arrival of the detectives.

The first detectives assigned to the case had had the sense to place a large table top over the fireplace to prevent disarrangement of any of the ashes. The fire had died out. It remained for Coldstream to make careful examination and gain from it what clues he could.

Among the warm embers were found the remains of various things which must have been cast into the fire between 1.10 and 5 p.m. These were: part of a carton which had contained Player's Navy Cut cigarettes, the sculptor's favourite brand; several sales circulars from artists' supply houses; bits of tinfoil paper supposed to have come from wild cherry lozenges, a half package of which was found in Lamont's pocket; and the perplexing bit of paper which is reproduced here:

To his great credit, Detective Coldstream was able to solve the mysterious crime, deducing both the identity of the guilty one and the motive for the killing with uncanny precision. Throwing the suspect off her guard, he confronted her with the damning evidence. She broke down, and confession followed.

What would you have deduced? The questions to be answered are:

1. *Who   murdered   Reginald   Lamont?* (Credit 2.)

2. *How did Coldstream deduce it?* (Credit 5.)

3. *What   probably   was   the   murderess's motive?* (Credit 1.)

4. *How   did   the   detective   deduce   that?* (Credit 2.)

Credit Score:

THE BEALS-BLIGH ANONYMOUS LETTERS

Who was the person that sent two anonymous threatening letters to Sir Chatham Beals-Bligh?

When Sir Chatham Beals-Bligh, well known in London society, married the rich Miss Millicent Packer of Seattle, Wash., he resolved to give up his life of man-about-town and settle down to more serious pursuits. Accordingly he refurbished the family estate at Tirringham (fifty miles from London) and laid plans to stand for Parliament. There he lived with his bride for nearly a year.

"A one-sided match," said the wiseacres, "he cares less than she does." And so it proved, for when the excitement of superintending the renovations was over, Sir Chatham found time hanging heavy on his hands. His neighbours were dull country squires, and he recalled with envy his former gay life in town.

At length, pleading that business necessitated a town visit, he came to London and stopped at his town house.

At the theatres and at his clubs he was hailed as one returning from the dead. Weeks passed into months, and Sir Chatham found it hard to return to his wife and the life at Tirringham. Indeed it soon became common gossip about town that Sir Chatham had resumed relations with a certain Austrian baroness, at whose home before his marriage he had been seen frequently.

To Sir Chatham's valet, Hobbs, this was a most unsatisfactory state of affairs, for he had recently become engaged to Suzette, Lady Beals-Bligh's young and charming French maid. And Hobbs, being a middle-aged and somewhat bald man, was afraid that in his continued absence Suzette might yield to the attractions of one of the younger servants.

At 10 a.m. one day in the third month of his absence from Tirringham, while telephoning to his wife at the Tirringham house, Sir Chatham was surprised to hear Lady Beals-Bligh announce her intention of coming to town the following day. It was clear to Sir Chatham that she was not to be wheedled out of carrying through the trip, and late that afternoon he set out on a last evening of freedom. Hobbs, who had asked for the evening off, departed from the house a few minutes later.

Sir Chatham returned shortly after midnight. Glancing, through habit, at the hall table where his mail was left by the servants in his absence from the house, he noticed a long envelope on which his name and address were written in crude block letters, all capitals. He tore open the envelope and with surprise and anger read the following unsigned note. Handprinted, it gave Sir Chatham no clue to the identity of the sender:

All your plans will be ruined if you continue this dishonorable affair, since I have incontrovertable proof, and will use it where it will do the most harm, if it is necessary.

The letter was postmarked 10.30 a.m. of that day, Paddington Station, London. Summoning the butler from his bed, Sir Chatham learned that it had arrived in the mail a few minutes after his departure from the house.

Sir Chatham smoked his pipe furiously before the fire. Who was dipping into his affairs? Was it blackmail? Could Hobbs be a traitor? He rang for the valet, but the housekeeper said Hobbs was still out.

At any rate, Sir Chatham reasoned, Hobbs could not have posted the letter at the Paddington Station just before 10.30 that morning, for he had attended Sir Chatham constantly from 7.30 until noon. And Sir Chatham knew that the mail boxes at Paddington were cleared every half hour. "Hobbs could not have left the house long enough to have mailed the letter there—not Hobbs, of all persons," Sir Chatham concluded, for the valet had been devoted to him for seven years.

Fifteen minutes later Hobbs arrived, out of breath from hurrying. He explained that he had spent the evening at Staines. He said he had missed the last train and had had to return by motor 'bus. Sir Chatham forebore to question him that night, but decided to watch him carefully.

The following morning Sir Chatham was amazed to receive, in the first delivery of the mail, another envelope of the same type, addressed in hand-printed block letters which resembled those in the anonymous note of the day before. But minute examination showed clearly that they were not from the same hand; the second note was only a fair imitation of the first. Its message was short:

What I mean is, I will tell your wife if it does not stop.

To his astonishment, the letter was post-marked Staines, the previous evening—Staines, the very suburb where Hobbs had missed his train the night before. In a sudden rage Sir Chatham Beals-Bligh accused the valet of having sent the letters and confronted him with both. Hobbs was shocked and protested in the most violent terms that he was innocent and specifically that he had no knowledge of the existence of the letters until they were laid before him. He said that he had gone alone to Staines, where he often went on his evenings off, when in London, to play cards with a friend, Raoul Gascoigne, keeper of a well-known French hotel on the banks of the Thames at Staines.

Sir Chatham was deeply affected by Hobbs's outburst, and, upon thinking it over, regretted his accusations. He reasoned that the valet surely could not have been so great a fool as to have told him on the previous evening that he had been at Staines if he had had knowledge that the second letter would bear the Staines postmark. Sir Chatham was baffled.

At noon Lady Beals-Bligh and her maid Suzette arrived at the town house. Alone in their apartment, his wife greeted him so affectionately that Sir Chatham impulsively decided upon a daring step. In fear that the anonymous threat might be carried out, he poured out his heart to his wife, telling her of the letters, making a clean breast of his relations with the baroness, and throwing himself on his wife's mercy. He gave assurances that he loved only her and that she need never fear a similar "indiscretion," which he said he deeply repented.

Lady Beals-Bligh received his confession in silence, and then without a word rose and left the room. An hour later she and her maid departed in a cab with her luggage.

Angered alternately at his confession and the rejection of it by his wife, Sir Chatham summoned his counsellor at law, an old friend, and laid the anonymous letters before him with instructions that the identity of the sender be discovered at all costs. He also gave instructions that handwriting experts be called on the case. A searching investigation was immediately requested of a private detective, former Inspector Givott, quondam anonymous letter expert of Scotland Yard. The counsellor at law promised a full report to Sir Chatham within a few days.

The following morning, while fully expecting that his wife's next communication would be through her solicitor, Sir Chatham was amazed to receive a letter postmarked Tirringham. It was an affectionate and philosophical letter from his wife, written the night before; it closed with this paragraph:

. . . and so, Chat, my dear, though at first I thought I could never forgive you, especially when you referred to your unfaithfulness as " an indiscretion," I do not think that God ever intended us to seperate, and if you really mean what you said to-day, come home and we will begin a new life, for I have been very unhappy since I left London, just as I know you have been since I went away—haven't you, darling?

Ever your loving wife,

Millicent.

With an unaccustomed alacrity and cheerfulness, Hobbs thought, Sir Chatham Beals-Bligh ordered the immediate packing of his bags and announced the welcome news that they were to leave for Tirringham. Sir Chatham called at the office of his counsellor and showed him the forgiveness letter. He placed a sum at the disposal of the investigating detective and ordered the result of the search to be forwarded to him at Tirringham. And he and Hobbs departed.

Three days later Sir Chatham's counsellor replied that the private detective could make no headway on the case whatever. And he added the opinion that unless annoyed by further anonymous letters, Sir Chatham might just as well let the matter rest.

And Sir Chatham did just that.

What do you make of the mystery? The questions to be answered are:

1. *Who sent the anonymous letters?* (Credit 2.)

2. *How is the sender's identity logically deduced?* (Credit 5.)

3. *Was there an accomplice to the act?* (Credit 3.)

Credit Score:

No. 11

MESSER BELLINI'S REPORT TO THE DOGE

A fascinating problem in crime detection is to be found in the Twelfth Century document recently authenticated by Professor Paolo Capelli of the University of Milan, which deals with the murder of one Giacomo Geronimo, evidently a favourite adviser of the Doge (or Duke) of Venice in the latter part of the century. The sketch and the portions of the text of the report printed here are taken from the old English translation, known since 1530 and probably of earlier origin. For all practical purposes the version is identical with the Capelli translation.

Being the Report of Messer Marco Bellini Made Privately to His Excellency, The Worshipful Aberno Arbasini, God's Knight of the Cross and Reverend Doge of Venice, in the Year of Our Lord 1189, on the Third of the Month December:

" WORSHIPFUL SIR:
" Mindful of Your Excellency's most

gracious command, your servant, I, have caused to be inquired into the untimely and abominable death of Your Excellency's quondam Minister and true friend (God rest His Soul!), the valiant Geronimo, for that Your Excellency hath suspicion that his death was caused not by his own hand as some have it but by the cunning encompassment of his enemies. And mindful of Your Excellency's command I have set aside the reports of others of the household who made pretence of inquiries, and have discovered now the solemn truth of this fearsome deed.

"Know, Worshipful Sir, that it was by the hand of the Cavaliere himself that the brave Geronimo was snared to his death, and in a villainous, cunning and subtile manner which, if it be not disclosed, will imperil all citizens of the Republic upon whom this Torcello's jealousy and evil spirit falls. For it was a dreadful deed and of the guiltiness of the Cavaliere Torcello there can be no longer doubt, seeing the repute of my informants and the dove-tailing of their separate testimonies. Which testimonies are, to wit:

"*The oath of Fernando, the poetaster, whose wretched rhymes could come only*

from a simple mind which could not be
guileful if it would:

"'For the Worshipful Messer Bellini, I swear, that I was guest at the dinner of the Cavaliere Torcello whereat the valiant Geronimo met his death, and have suspicions that it was from the wine then and there drunk that he died and not from the lavendered sugar which he carried and ate of custom, which latter was first reported and is widely cherished by the populace. And my reasons for this are, namely: that I too ate of the Worshipful Geronimo's lavendered sugar freely when he offered me his box on the terrace of the Cavaliere's *palazzo*, we having entered together, and naught of any harm came to me therefrom.

"'So that those who say that the valiant Geronimo died from sugar which he alone did eat, do err, forasmuch as I also ate. And those who say that it could not have been from the wine drunk, forasmuch as the Cavaliere poured for all guests from the same pitcher, they also err, since of this pitcher something happened of which none wot save I and the girl Baptista. But it is not clear in my head, for I was much drunk and enamoured of the girl Baptista as well. Yet she can tell without doubt, for it was she who blew into the pitcher and it was then that the bubble came and we were affrighted and left the table. No more will I say, but she can tell and will, since the Cavaliere but last week cast her off.'

"No more, Your Excellency, could I gain from this Ferando, he being a timid one and easily affrighted. Yet look upon the testimony of Baptista, the harlot, a shrewd and honest girl who would be a dancer:

"*The oath of Baptista Vittore, late of the household of the Cavaliere Calergi Torcello:*

"'For the Worshipful Messer Bellini, I swear, that I was bidden to the dinner whereat the valiant Geronimo met his death, being told by my master, the Cavaliere, to attend and observe the manners of the gentles that I might learn from them, though if what I saw that night amongst the ladies of Venice be graces, may I never be a lady, since I know sin when I see it as well as the next.

"'And that the valiant Geronimo was poisoned to his death I do not doubt, and all from a pitcher bewitched (God Save the Mark!) from the hands of the Cavaliere himself. And the events fell out in this way: that a dozen of company was present and the Cavaliere poured a precious wine from a pitcher and made a great show of serving all from the same pitcher and did it ever with his own hands. And all drank and were warmed and thereafter for long all drank from cups ever refilled from the Cavaliere's pitcher, and this ever and anon filled from a wineskin. And all made merry and called each other friend, and I did watch the Cavaliere closely when he would pour for Geronimo and nothing did he put stealthily in Geronimo's cup or in the pitcher, for all were openly looking.

" 'Yet soon after a pouring, mayhap the twelfth or the twentieth, I know not which, and whilst the merriment was at its height, I beheld the valiant Geronimo clutch at his stomach, and several friends bore him to another room, but all thought him drunk and that was all, for much wine had been drunk, nor did I think aught amiss. And the Cavaliere made great ado to ease the pain of the valiant Geronimo and swore that it was a pity that a man should mix lavendered sugar with his drinking as Geronimo had done.

" 'And at that time, when the Cavaliere was in the next room, and all the others drunk and fondling, this Fernando, the rhymester, was pawing at me and I cried to mock him:

" ' Nay, I will not kiss thee! I will kiss my own true love which is this wine-pitcher!'

" ' And then, for a jest, I leaned to the pitcher standing on the table and made as if to kiss its lip whence the wine issued, but

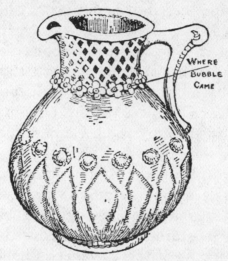

WHERE
BUBBLE
CAME

Sketch of the wine pitcher used by the Cavaliere Torcello as described in Messer Bellini's report to the Doge

Fernando at this moment tugging my arm, I could not reach it with my lips, but falling somewhat short I blew under the lip of the pitcher, laughing loudly.

" ' And then a strange thing happened, for even as I blew, a great glistening dark bubble came on the side of the pitcher, swelling out from one of the blossoms which adorned the vessel near to the handle of it. And then it burst and, from whence it had come, a black drop oozed. And Fernando and I were amazed and we knew that the pitcher was bewitched, for the wine therein was not of that hue but a palish red. And I broke away from the rhymester and fled from the room, nor will I go again to the Torcello *palazzo* though the whole college of cardinals go with me, since I mistrust the Cavaliere and his cunning smiles. For ere I fled to my room Geronimo had died in agony.' "

And now, Worshipful Sir, comes that which binds the deed to this smiling villain whose ill-will we have had cause enough to guess. For, my suspicions aroused, I have covertly sought from a servant of the Cavaliere's household a further description of this strange pitcher and . . .

———

To quote further from Messer Bellini's report would reveal to the reader too plainly the explanation of the mystery which had baffled the Doge's investigator. How do you explain the death of Giacomo Geronimo, and the Venetian wine pitcher? How came the dark bubble and what did it mean?

On page 81 is reproduced a sketch of the celebrated vessel, the first known of its kind. The sketch was drawn from the painting accompanying the manuscript of Messer Marco Bellini's report. Examine it carefully and answer the following questions:

1. *How was Torcello able to single out Geronimo from the other guests in administering the poison?* (Credit 5.)

2. *What probably would have happened to Baptista if she had helped herself to wine?* (Credit 2.)

3. *Why was the fretwork of the pitcher open everywhere except near the lip of the pitcher?* (Credit 3.)

Credit Score:

THE MYSTERY OF THE MURDERED PHYSICIAN

Was Dr. Brett's murderer a man or a woman? Even this much the police never determined. But Inspector Marquard, late of Scotland Yard, has revived interest in this celebrated, unsolved mystery by the statement in his recently published reminiscences, that the sex of the murderer was conclusively indicated by evidence available from the very first. What is your opinion?

Dr. Winthrop Brett, of Mayfair, it will be recalled, was among the first English physicians to journey to Vienna for tutelage when the fame of Freud began spreading through knowing medical circles early in the century. By 1926 the Mayfair psycho-analyst had fairly skimmed the cream of the wealthy, select patronage in his region, and had amassed a fortune so large that cynical ones whispered talk of blackmail as an adjunct to his specialty. Among the newspaper men of Fleet Street, the physician's now famous "little green books" had long been a by-word, and to them, at least, his murder was not the most unexpected of things. It was common gossip among them that there were a half dozen men or women who might have had sufficient motive to commit the crime.

The first notice of the murder of Dr. Brett came from Wilkins, the physician's valet, who telephoned the police at 6.5 p.m. in the greatest excitement. (It was on November 22nd, a chilly day.) He said that he had just returned from an afternoon off and had found his employer shot dead in the private study of his bachelor flat. The police ordered Wilkins to touch nothing in the flat pending the arrival of detectives.

Fifteen minutes later, police entered the private study in the flat. Brett's body was lying on its left side, back against the wall, directly below the wall safe. The victim had been shot twice from a .25 calibre automatic. One bullet had entered the abdomen; the other, the right lung. The lung wound had caused a hæmorrhage. A great crimson stain of blood covered the entire front of the physician's grey, double-breasted coat from collar to waist and extended to the heavy greyish-blue rug on the floor.

Medical examination later revealed that he must have been dead for more than an hour. It was observed that although the pockets of the physician's clothes had been rummaged, his gold watch and £15 in notes were untouched. His keys, however, were missing and were never found.

The wall-safe, 5 feet from the floor, below which the physician's body was found had been opened—undoubtedly with keys removed from the dead man's pocket, for it had not been forced. Examination revealed that a small black steel box had been removed and replaced. From this black steel box the small green leather-covered books had been taken, according to the deductions of the police. It was within these books that Dr. Brett kept many of his private case records, and it was presumed (and never has been disproved) that they rested within the steel box as usual on the day of the murder.

The alibi of Wilkins, the valet, from 2.30 that afternoon until he telephoned the police, was early established by the detectives and cannot be questioned. In fact, it should be said that no justifiable suspicion of Wilkins, either as a principal or as an accomplice in the crime, has ever been established by any evidence, and it may be assumed that Wilkins told everything that he knew.

The detailed examination of Wilkins brought out the interesting fact that the physician had made an appointment for three o'clock that afternoon with a person who had telephoned at about one o'clock. Wilkins's testimony follows:

"The doctor didn't go to his consulting room in Wimpole Street on Tuesdays, so he was home here this morning. He went out for lunch at twelve and returned just before one. I was in the private study putting some books in the closet for him when his private telephone rang. That is the one on his desk. It is not connected with the flat's switchboard.

"He was sitting at the desk and he answered it himself. He didn't greet anyone; he wasn't surprised or angry. He was very matter-of-fact, and I never noticed *what* he said except when he called me and said:

"'Wilkins, you may have the afternoon off until six!'

"The doctor sometimes said that to me suddenly, and I was always glad to go whenever the opportunity came. He was still holding the wire when he said that to me. Yes, I am quite sure he resumed conversation on the 'phone *after* saying that to me, for when I came out of the closet later, I remember him laying down the 'phone. Then he said:

"'You can go at 2.30, Wilkins. I have an appointment for three and I shall be dressing for dinner at eight. You may stay away until six.'

" So I left him then and didn't get back till after six. I always followed orders with Dr. Brett. He often had confidential appointments with lots of people, you understand, and I always followed orders exactly."

The detectives proceeded with a minute examination of the private study, but they found no fingerprints. The highly polished surface of the black steel box, the wall-safe door, and the doctor's black wallet—all these, which must have been examined and touched by the murderer—had been wiped clean of fingerprints, as if with a wet cloth.

A damp towel was found over the handle of the door leading into the bathroom adjoining. It was also noted that the cold water at the bathroom wash basin was still running (about one quarter on). Wilkins testified that it was

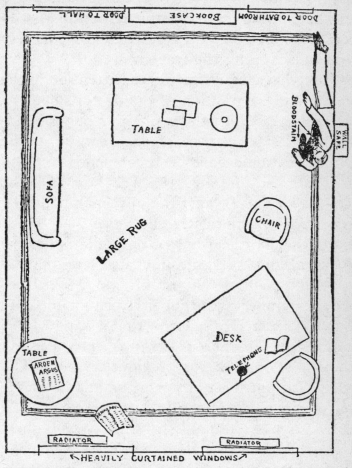

Police diagram of Dr. Brett's private study, showing where the body of the murdered physician was found. (Courtesy of Scotland Yard)

thus when he first inspected the apartment at 6.5. In this he was corroborated by the negro lift operator of the apartment building, who had answered Wilkin's startled cry for help upon discovering the tragedy.

But what most attracted the attention of the police was the position of the doctor's body as it lay, back against the wall, on the floor below the wall-safe. It was apparent that the murderer would have been compelled to reach over the body to open the wall-safe. On the desk lay a novel—as if the physician had been reading when his visitor entered.

On the floor near one of the radiators of the room, a single sheet of newspaper was found—the back page of that morning's *Daily Mail*. The remainder of the paper lay on a table near by. The detectives noted that a part of the single sheet of newspaper was shrivelled, as though it had been previously wet. The shrivelled portion ran down the middle of the paper almost from top to bottom, for a little more than a column's width. When questioned, Wilkins, the valet, was certain that the *Daily Mail* was complete and untorn on the table when he left at 2.30.

Scrupulous examination of the physician's flat yielded no further clues. Nothing of importance was gleaned from the neighbouring flats, either from the liftman, or from the switchboard operator. No one remembered either a man or a woman calling at the Brett flat—either going or coming—at any time during the afternoon. This was not extraordinary, however, for the flat was on the ground floor and it was not, necessary to pass the lift operators or switchboard operator in order to ring the doctor's bell and gain entrance. No shots had been heard.

The net deductions of the police were as follows; and since Inspector Marquard agrees they may be assumed correct.

1. The murderer came by appointment at three o'clock, stayed for an hour or more and then shot the physician.

2. The murderer robbed the wall safe and erased the fingerprints *without haste*, apparently secure in the knowledge that the valet, Wilkins, would not return for some time and that disturbance from anyone else was a remote possibility.

The police, at the time, held it impossible to do more than guess at the sex of the murderer. But Inspector Marquard says that evidence affording clues to the murderer's *actions* in the flat *after* the shooting, proves conclusively the sex of the murderer.

What do you deduce?   Don't guess ; reason it out.

The questions to be answered are:

1. *Was a man or a woman the murderer of Dr. Brett?* (Credit 1.)

2. *What conclusively proves the sex of the murderer?* (Credit 9.)

Credit Score:

THE AFFAIR OF THE FRENCH SPY

During the World War many subtle brains were devoted to originating secret forms of communication, and also to detecting the new codes and ciphers used for communication by the enemy. An episode illustrating the keenness of the secret agents in this " underworld combat " between espionage and counter espionage occurred in Switzerland. It presents an interesting problem.

A certain Mlle. G., an agent of the French, had been assigned to the French counter espionage service; that is, to the branch of the Secret Service which spies upon spies. In Berne, in Zurich, and Geneva, Mlle. G. posed so successfully as a Swiss lady that she succeeded in gaining the confidence of German espionage agents. These sought to engage her as a German agent to spy upon the French. For her, this was extraordinary luck; she accepted their offer, and her French superiors

were delighted. Her reports to the French became increasingly valuable since she was now
gaining important information from the
Germans while pretending to serve them.

One day, however, the French counter
espionage headquarters was shocked to learn
through Belgian sources that some one of their
trusted agents on the French espionage payroll
had proved treacherous to them and was in
reality serving German agents—that is, had
become a double spy and was deceiving them,
even as Mlle. G., their agent, was a double spy
deceiving the German adversary.

The French immediately grew anxious to
discover the identity of this treacherous agent
so that he might be arrested at once. They
secretly informed Mlle. G. of the situation and
ordered her to lose no time in seeking this
essential information, without, however, in any
way betraying herself to the German agents in
Switzerland with whom she was now daily
associating.

By surreptitious examination of documents
in the official files of her German associates,
Mlle. G. managed to learn the identity of the
treacherous spy just an hour before she was due
to leave Berne on an important commission for
her German employers. If she were to get her

Mlle. G. as she awaited her confederate in the lobby of the hotel

important information to her French employers quickly enough for them to seize the traitor, it was necessary that she do so before the hour was up, for after that she would be constantly in the company of the Germans. She could not telegraph the message, for she knew that the telegraph offices were honeycombed with espionage agents of all countries, and if any of them decoded the message it might lead to her own discovery. Mail would be too late.

There was one chance: fortunately, Mlle. G. had arranged an appointment in her hotel lobby with one of her French confederates in Berne so that she might give him, if necessary, the latest information before she left. But she felt certain that she and her visitors were watched at all times, so it had been arranged that her confederate should take a seat near her in the hotel lobby, but not take the initiative in addressing her.

In short, Mlle. G. was faced with the difficult problem of conveying a vital message upon very short notice to a confederate who could be near her and watch her, but with whom she might not dare to hold conversation. Indeed, in view of the certain presence in the lobby of German agents who might be watching her closely, she knew that she must not be seen nodding significantly, signalling by hand, or doing anything which might arouse their suspicions.

In spite of the difficulties confronting her, Mlle. G. acquainted her confederate with the identity of the treacherous French spy and without attracting attention. And within ten hours the spy was under arrest.

How did she do it? The accompanying sketch shows Mlle. G. as she sat in the main salon of a well-known hotel in Berne. She stayed there for only five minutes, reading a book. Her confederate seated near her got the communication, yet there was no talk between them. She returned to her room unsuspected.

The questions to be answered are:

1. *How did Mlle. G. communicate the message to her confederate?* (Credit 7.)

2. *What was the text of the message?* (Credit 3.)

Credit Score:

THE SHOOTING OF "WHISPER" MALLOY

One of the most interesting detective problems that ever confronted the Surrey police was found last year in the circumstances of the so-called "Hog's Back killings." The police were first informed of the tragedy by James Haynes, a Guildford milkman. Haynes, while driving up to the crest of the Hog's Back, just where it takes a rare curve, found an open car on the side of the road. The time was 6 a.m. and the sun had only just risen, and there was no traffic along the Hog's Back at that hour. In the front seat of the car were two dead men. The Guildford police could not identify them, but a Scotland Yard detective, who was down working on an important country house burglary—one of a long series of such—was able to do so at once.

The body sprawled over the steering wheel was that of "Whisper" Malloy, a denizen of the underworld, who had played the part of informer to the London police for several years.

The body next it was that of "Long Dan" Shutz, a notorious American criminal and sworn enemy of the informer, who had once been the cause of his getting a stiff sentence in England. It was "Whisper's" car.

"Whisper" had been shot in the forehead, just above the left eye, with a bullet from an Enfield rifle. The coroner established that he must have been rendered unconscious immediately and that he must have died a very few seconds later. On the road at the right side of the car (see accompanying diagram) lay an Enfield rifle. The bullet found in Malloy's skull at the autopsy was later identified by rifle experts as having been fired from this rifle.

The police were amazed to observe that the tall, pock-marked youth, known as "Long Dan" Shutz, had been shot from the right side, two bullets having entered his neck. A Winchester rifle lay between the two bodies, close beside "Whisper's" sprawled form. The stock of the Winchester rested on the leather-cushioned seat, almost touching the right hip of the informer; its barrel point rested on the low wind shield. The autopsy on the body of

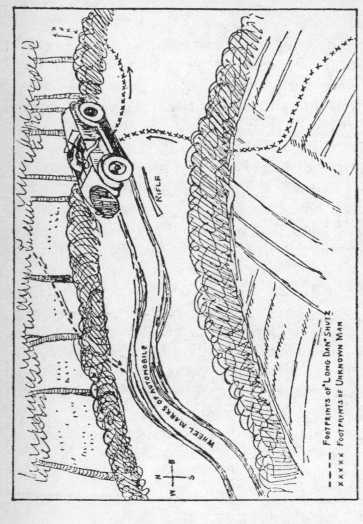

The tell-tale scene on the Hog's Back, reconstructed according to data furnished by the Guildford police

RIFLE

WHEEL MARKS OF AUTOMOBILE

- - - Footprints of "Long Dan" Shutz
x x x x Footprints of Unknown Man

100

Shutz identified the two bullets which had slain him as having come from this Winchester rifle.

Just what had happened? A duel? How came the enemy of the murdered informer into the car? And which died first? There were no clear fingerprints on either rifle. "Whisper" had on gloves; "Long Dan" had none.

The police were able to make out (on the surface of the highway and its neighbouring fields) many footprints which aided in a partial solution of the mystery. The automobile tracks were also studied.

The detectives knew that both victims were men with more than one enemy, but they had scarcely expected to see them die together under such mystifying circumstances. What do you deduce?

The questions to be answered are:

1. *Who killed "Whisper" Malloy?* (Credit 2.)

2. *Who killed "Long Dan" Shutz?* (Credit 2.)

3. *Which was shot first?* (Credit 1.)

4. *How came " Long Dan " in the informer's car?* (Credit 3.)

5. *Why did the unknown man go to the car?* (Credit 2.)

Credit Score:

No. 15

THE PROBLEM OF NAPOLEON'S SIGNATURES

What does handwriting tell you? Here is a pretty problem involving deductions from signatures of Napoleon Bonaparte penned at various crises in his amazing career. According to the late Hans Gross, famous authority on crime detection, it is possible to deduce from each autograph the state of Napoleon's mind and of his fortunes at the time of making.

Referring to the revelations of handwriting, Dr. Gross writes in his authoritative *Handbook of Criminal Investigation:*

"The most difficult thing to do is to compare, not the writing of persons of different character, but those of the same person in different moods. With much reason the various signatures of Napoleon are usually cited in this connection. Few men have experienced so strongly as he the whole gamut of impressions. Few have seen so many events. . . . What changes in destiny! What changes of disposition! What changes *in writing!*

" Study of the signatures is more instructive than a whole shelf full of books. It seems quite impossible to confound the dates of the various signatures and mistake those of the zenith of the fortunes of Bonaparte for that made at St. Helena."

On page 107 you will find facsimiles of eight authentic signatures of Napoleon I, made at various times. What do you deduce from them? What phases of his eventful career do they denote?

Dates of the signatures are withheld, but as a guide to solution of the problem, descriptive captions are given (one for each signature). It is for you to say if you can which caption belongs under each signature. This may be too difficult, however, for anyone but a handwriting expert, so the problem is confined to the following questions, which should be answered:

1. *Which was Napoleon's signature as General-in-Chief of the Egyptian Expedition in 1798 (before he became Emperor)?* (Credit 2.)

2. *Which when he first became Emperor, in 1804?* (Credit 3.)

3. *Which at Tilsit in 1807 (when all Europe but England lay at his mercy)?* (Credit 2.)

4. *Which at Elba in 1814 (his voluntary exile)?* (Credit 2.)

5. *Which at St. Helena in 1815 (the beginning of his enforced exile)?* (Credit 1.)

Credit Score:

THE FOLLOWING CAPTIONS INDICATE THE VARYING STATES OF MIND AND OF FORTUNES OF NAPOLEON BONAPARTE AT THE TIMES OF THE MAKING OF THE SIGNATURES. AT VARIOUS STAGES OF HIS CAREER NAPOLEON SIGNED HIMSELF DIFFERENTLY: "N," "BONAPARTE" "NAPOL.," "NAPOLEON," ETC. WHICH SIGNA-TURE BELONGS TO WHAT PARTICULAR PERIOD? WHAT DO YOU DEDUCE FROM THE HAND-WRITING?

Before he became Emperor. Still a general. Written as Commander of the Egyptian Expedition in 1798.

Done very soon after becoming Emperor, in 1804. He had been First Consul or actual ruler of France for several years. Age 35.

A few days before his abdication as Emperor (just before voluntary exile on Elba). Done April 4, 1814.

Done two months after arriving at St. Helena on his forced and final exile. Date December, 1816.

At the Imperial Camp at Tilsit, 1807, when the Emperor had virtually all Europe, except England, at his mercy. Perhaps the climax of his military successes, but the beginning of the tremendous egotism of a world conqueror.

September, 1814. From the island of Elba where Napoleon went in voluntary exile. In a few months he retrieved his fortunes dramatically by returning. Then Waterloo.

Done at Berlin, October 29, 1806. At the very height of his career. In 1805 he had conquered Austria. In 1806, Prussia. He was still thinking clearly. Egotism had not yet dominated.

Done October 1, 1813. Bonaparte's enemies were slowly but surely wearing him down. Several of his armies commanded by his marshals had been defeated. Yet he was not to be beaten decisively until 1815.

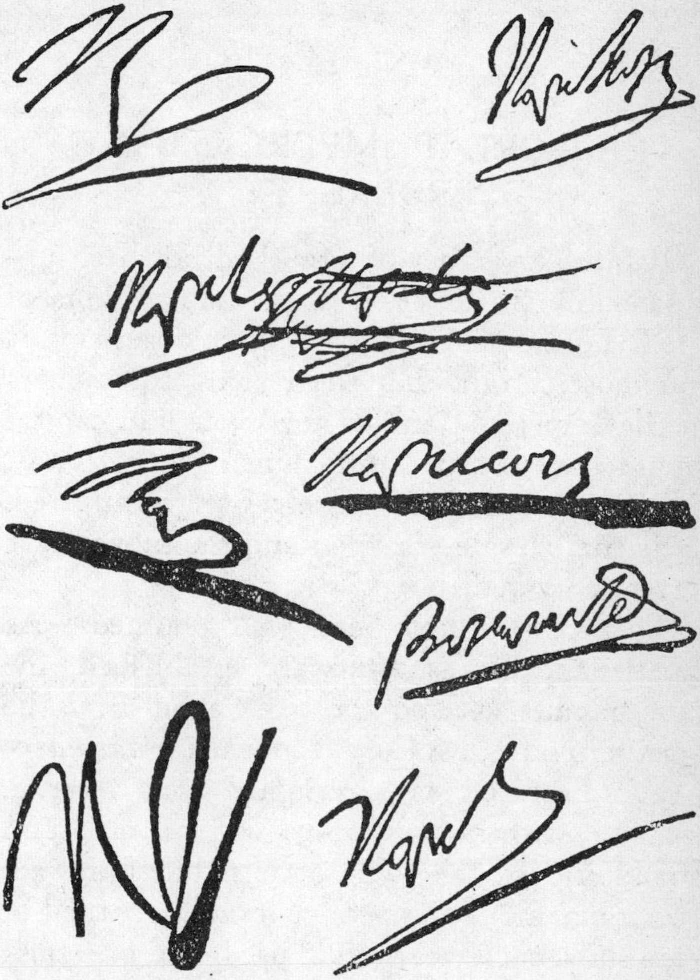

THE GREAT IMPERIAL BANK ROBBERY

If late November of 1926 had not been unseasonably warm, or if Lieutenant Elkins of the Ottawa police had not been so observant, it is almost certain that the resourceful robbers of the Imperial Bank of the Canadian capital would have escaped punishment. As it was, though the bandits themselves were captured, their confederates escaped and the money was never recovered.

The robbery had been well planned. As Lieutenant Elkins afterward established, the four bandits entered the bank soon after the opening hour. McCory, the leader, was effectively disguised as a crippled war veteran, limping with a hesitancy which was soon abandoned in the swift action that followed. His companions were conventionally garbed in blue suits, each wearing a false beard or moustache; and two wore spectacles.

The alluring objective was the acquisition of

three large factory payrolls which the robbers knew were being prepared at that hour for representatives of the factories. These, totalling $54,000, were swept into bags within a few seconds of the beginning of the well-timed and cold-blooded àssault. The men dashed out, leaped into a black racing car, and were around the corner before anyone dared to spread the alarm. Police followed in commandeered cars, but they lost the trail within a few minutes in the morning traffic and were baffled to know which way to proceed.

Ten minutes later police headquarters received word from a suburban section that an automobile containing four men was speeding on one of the highways to the north of the city. Lieutenant Elkins was rushed to the spot and picked up there a brief description of the car. The informant was able to point out the exact tracks made by the car. Lieutenant Elkins followed them, having left instructions to telephone ahead to all possible destinations on the road taken by the speeding car and have police of the various communities head it off.

There was little difficulty in following the track of the car. Its distinctive tyre impressions led seven miles due north on the main highway, then a mile to the west on the broad, dusty Derham road, flanked by level meadows. At this point the car's tracks mingled with other tyre tracks, which baffled the pursuers for a distance of about a third of a mile.

However, certain that the fleeing car could have gone on in only one way, Elkins directed his driver to forge ahead, and at the end of the one-third mile stretch the car's distinctive tracks again appeared alone in the road.

A few minutes later he reached the town of Derham and there learned that a touring car containing four men had driven through in leisurely fashion twenty minutes before. Their descriptions, however, differed so radically from those broadcast by the Ottawa police that the local constable had not interfered with them. None had a beard or moustache or glasses, and all four were chatting gaily. They had been observed by several persons, and a fair description had been gleaned: two wore light grey tweed suits and overcoats; the other two, brown clothes. They were young, and the constable had taken them for college students on an outing.

Lieutenant Elkins wisely telephoned ahead to Wheatonville and had them arrested on suspicion. They indignantly denied all knowledge of the crime and invited search for their

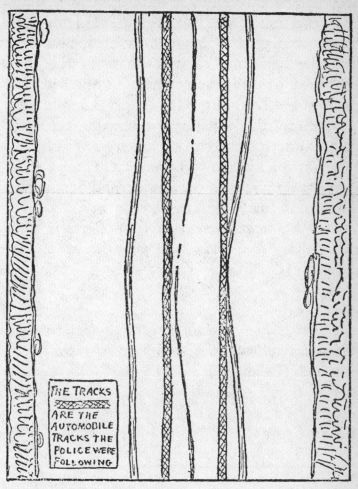

THE TRACKS
ARE THE
AUTOMOBILE
TRACKS THE
POLICE WERE
FOLLOWING

*Segment of the broad, dusty Derham road showing mysterious tracks
discovered by Lieutenant Elkins in pursuing the robbers of the
Imperial Bank. Grass at extreme left and right*

persons and of the motor-car. Nothing whatever incriminating was found.   Lieutenant
Elkins managed to have them held, however,
until he had time to investigate further the
confusion of tyre tracks which had baffled him
back on the Derham road. After some thought
and study the mystery was explained.   A
diagrammatic sketch of a section of the
Derham road is shown on page 111.

What do you deduce? What had happened?
The questions to be answered are:

1. *What had happened on the Derham road
where the confusion of tyre tracks baffled
Elkins?* (Credit 7.)

2. *What step should a good detective have
taken immediately in an effort to recover the
money?* (Credit 3.)

Credit Score:

THE PROBLEM AT THE ABANDONED BUNGALOW

Towards the end of a day in the summer of 1927, the police received a tip from under-world sources that a gang of alleged cocaine smugglers might be found at a certain abandoned bungalow on the Essex coast. In spite of elaborate precautions of the police, who hoped to surprise the gang, the bungalow when surrounded was found deserted. The occupants had apparently been tipped off in their turn by someone who knew what was to happen.

It was a one-room bungalow, long since abandoned by its owners. Almost all the furniture had been removed. The detectives were confronted by the problem of deducing, from the evidence in the room, the size of the gang and some characteristics of its members.

The room was furnished merely with four kitchen chairs, a wooden packing box, a rickety table, and some old crockery. The only clues available were as follows:

Besides many matches of the ordinary paper
    type on the floor about the table, there
    there were twenty-odd burned, large-sized
    wooden matches scattered on the floor
    behind one of the chairs.
Stubs of five Turkish cigarettes and four
    cigarettes made from Virginia tobacco.
One cigar butt, Corona-Perfecto.
The four chairs and the wooden packing box
    placed around the table as shown in the
    accompanying sketch.
A bottle of iodine, nine-tenths full, with several
    drops of iodine on the seat of the chair on
    which it stood.
The cigarette- and cigar-stubs were scattered,
    some on the floor, some by the cups that
    stood on the table.

Closer examination of the cups showed that
they had contained a good brand of whisky.
Clearly defined on the wooden packing box
were a dozen or more small dents, equally
divided into two groups about six inches apart
—both groups some eight inches from the floor.
The dents were each about a quarter of an inch
long and less than a sixteenth of an inch deep
in the soft wood. The cigar butt was found by
the cup in front of the wooden box.

*Sketch from police photographs of the scene at the abandoned bunga-
low. (Courtesy of Capt. Farnsworth)*

Neither footprints nor finger-prints were in evidence. Nevertheless, the detectives were able to infer important characteristics of some of the occupants of the bungalow. Ultimately it resulted in the identification and capture of the gang.

Had you been there as a detective, what would you have deduced? The questions to be answered are:

1. *How many were in the gang?* (Credit 2.)

2. *What was a distinguishing characteristic of each member which might serve to identify the gang if seen by the police?* (Credit 8.)

Credit Score:

THE WARFIELD-COBHAM
JEWEL ROBBERY

Just one question concerned the police in the Warfield-Cobham case: was the butler an accomplice? How would you have answered it?

The early editions of the evening newspapers of Thursday, July 23rd, carried the first news of the robbery at Mrs. Henry Warfield-Cobham's country house. It was the sensation of the month. The wealthy widow, who had lived in virtual retirement since the death of her distinguished husband four years before, had been found that morning humanely but efficiently gagged and bound in her own bed, having been an eye-witness during the night to a £12,000 jewel robbery in her own bedroom on the second floor. A wall safe behind her dressing-table had been forced with chisel and crowbar before her eyes and emptied of its contents by a tall, broad-shouldered and courteous

individual who was immediately spotted by
the police from her description, as " Gentleman
Claude," alias François Marchesne, a notorious
Quebec cracksman commonly alleged to have
done equal time in prison and college, who had
lately been "working" in England. At any
rate, the police said, the job had been done with
the consummate courtesy characteristic of
" Gentleman Claude "—and the jewels were
gone.

The police were inclined to believe that the
robber must have had information, if not
actual assistance, from someone on the inside
of the house. But on this point Mrs. Warfield-
Cobham was firm: she refused to believe that
any of her staff of old servants could have been
implicated in the robbery. Present during the
detectives' questioning of them all, the lady of
the house openly expressed confidence in the
integrity of each. Each of the servants denied
any knowledge of the affair, and, apparently,
with the deepest sincerity. The police were
nettled.

Early in the afternoon following the robbery,
however, a tradesman of Chichester, the nearest
town to Mrs. Warfield-Cobham's home, came
to the police with the following story:

" I was walking along the Chichester road

last night about twelve o'clock, wheeling my motor-cycle. It had broken down. I saw a car in the woods opposite a big estate. It was driven up into the bushes so far, it looked as if someone wanted to hide it. I went up and looked at it, and found it was a Buick. Nobody was in it. I went on my way a hundred feet or so, and I thought I saw a man drop over the big wall of the estate.

" I didn't know whose estate it was. I waited awhile and laid down my machine and climbed up a tree. In the moonlight I could see the figure of a man moving stealthily from bush to bush, going toward the house. It was a big house. The man was very tall. I could see him, but he didn't see me. He was carrying something in his left hand about the size of a big club.

" All of a sudden, while he was waiting behind a bush, a light flashed, up near the top of the house. It flashed twice more—from up near the eaves. Then the big fellow stepped right out and walked boldly across the lawn and went around the side of the house. So I thought it must be all right—perhaps some lover or an elopement or something. I never thought it could be a robbery, because the light signals were so plain. But now I have read the papers and seen the picture of the house in the papers, and it was the Warfield-Cobham house all right. I wish I hadn't gone home so soon. I didn't hear any noise after that. I went on."

As a result of this report the police shadowed the Warfield-Cobham servants for more than

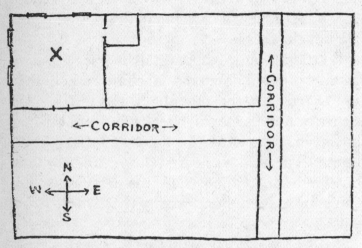

Floor plan of the second floor of Warfield-Cobham house. X marks the bedroom of Mrs. Warfield-Cobham

two weeks, but to no avail. Butler, gardener, chauffeur, cook, housekeeper, maids—by all their actions they were conventional and law-abiding individuals.

But finally there came to the police through that invisible telegraph system of the under-world—the informer—a vague tip that the butler, John Ardmore, had known " Gentleman Claude " of old.   And Sergeant Hodge, newly assigned to the case, managed to strike up a flirtation with one of the maids without revealing that he was a detective.   In the course of time he learned that Ardmore, on the Tuesday before the robbery, had sent a letter from the house to Portsmouth (fifteen miles) by the chauffeur!

The chauffeur, cornered by Hodge and two other policemen that evening, readily admitted taking the letter.   But he said that it could have had nothing to do with the robbery since it contained an advertisement to be inserted in the Portsmouth *Evening News*.   He said he had delivered it at the office of the paper, as requested by the butler.   It had contained a money order to pay for the advertisement, he said, and the envelope was addressed to the " Want Ad." Dept.

The chauffeur added:

" John told me the letter was important and must be delivered at once.   He said a friend had asked him to post it a few days ago and that he had forgotten to do it.   The writing on the envelope wasn't like John's.   I think you're all crazy.   Check it up at the newspaper office and you'll find that it was nothing but an ad."

Taking the chauffeur with him, Sergeant Hodge went to the office of the *Evening News*. The clerks there could give no clue as to *which* of the thousands of want ads. received on that particular day had come from the letter said to have been delivered by the chauffeur. But Hodge persevered. He searched all the columns of the *Evening News* of the day of the robbery. He found six advertisements which he decided were unusual enough to warrant a thorough examination for hidden meaning.

From the ads. herewith reproduced, Sergeant Hodge reached a very definite conclusion. What would you have deduced?

The questions to be answered are:

1. *Was the butler an accomplice in the robbery?* (Credit 1.)

2. *How could the detective be certain of the conclusion he reached?* (Credit 9.)

Credit Score:

Situations Wanted, Male

MANAGER'S ASSISTANT, varied experience, just back from tour, made for government bureau, desires return commercial life preferably South of England competent act second in command event manager's absence; business immaterial provided only that it offers a living salary and lucrative opportunity advancement within couple years. Available Wednesday. Wide general experience. Address Box 12 EVENING NEWS, Portsmouth.

Help Wanted, Male

LAND & HOUSE AGENTS can earn big money selling shrubbery, evergreens, trees, roses, &c., for planting next Autumn or Spring: free plans for landscape jobs, large and small; every home a prospect; no collecting; buyers pay after delivery; complete line of highest grade goods; wonderful selling material and full co-operation; excellent opportunity to connect permanently for full or part time on liberal commission basis with nationally known highly rated concern; this is a fine proposition. Y 2182. EVENING NEWS.

MANAGER FOR BROADCASTING STATION. A nationally known firm is desirous of securing the services of a manager for a broadcasting station; must be a high type executive capable of sales results; the man accepted will have to pass a rigid test as to character and responsibility; knowledge of the broadcasting field is desirable but not necessary; successful sales ability is required; send all information possible in first letter stating age, whether married or single. Z 2483. EVENING NEWS.

THERE IS available a most desirable connection for a salesman who is of the bigger type, who can intelligently present a unique service of extraordinary merit; the opportunity is with a highly successful organization, leaders in their field, with a high reputation for a quality product and a capable executive staff; previous advertising experience not necessary, but ability above the average is decidedly important; the type of man we seek may be employed at present and may feel sceptical about answering a blind advertisement, but you will find it worth while to satisfy us that you are big enough and interview will be arranged; commission and drawing account basis. Address A. M. 1210 New Street, Southampton.

Help Wanted, Female

YOUNG LADY, brunette, age not over twenty-five, weight not over 120 pounds, height about five feet, must be of pleasing personality, able and willing to appear in public places attired in French aviation costume for advertising purposes, account of exclusive hotel must furnish references. Z 2270. EVENING NEWS.

Business Connections

GERMAN MERCHANT, Partner, of old established Hamburg firm, with sales organization and first-class connections all over Germany and Morocco (North Africa); at present on short visit in Southampton; is desirous of taking up negotiations, representation of high-class concerns wanting an outlet in above countries also open for any other propositions to represent British interests in Germany. B 31. Portsmouth EVENING NEWS.

THE LA JOYA RIVER
HOMICIDE

Where Portos da Vega, the La Joya cowboy, met his death, the State police finally learned by very sensible methods of deduction. But they never caught the murderer because they did not determine quickly enough from which ranch his body had been thrown into the river. The slayer escaped and has never been heard of to this day. How would you have solved the problem which then confronted the State police?

Early on the morning of October 4th mill hands at the La Joya mill saw a dark object washed over the low dam of the river and become lodged between two rocks only fifty yards from the east bank of the river. They investigated and found that it was the body of a man, and brought it ashore at 6.20 a.m. The actual time of the sighting of the body as it washed over the dam was established as 6.13.

It proved to be the strangled body of Portos da Vega, a daring horseman and crack shot who had previously worked at various times for many of the ranchers whose ranches abutted on the river. Since all the ranches were on the east side of the river, and since the body came down so close to the east bank, it seemed clear that the victim had been thrown into the water from one of the ranches. It was also clear that the man had been strangled by a piece of rope before having entered the water. The coroner found no water in the lungs; the body had been floating.

The coroner pronounced that the body had been in the water " not less than forty minutes and not more than four hours," and that death had occurred before immersion. A search of the dead man's pockets yielded two illuminating clues: his watch and a scrap of paper. The watch was a cheap one of standard make. Its water-soaked hands pointed to 5.25, and it proved to be nearly wound up—lacking only three turns from being fully wound. From tests made on the spot with other watches of the same brand and type, it was determined that Da Vega's watch must have stopped within two to four minutes after immersion.

In the dead man's breeches pocket was found a small ball of paper, a fragment of a note handwritten in capital letters with a blue crayon pencil. Though soaked and smeared, it was recognisable. The fragment said:

RANCH, NORTH-WEST CORNER BY RIVER FENCE, AT 5.15 TO-MORROW MORNING IF YOU WANT THE STRAIGHT DOPE ON LA MOLLURA.

A FRIEND.

Now, it was well known that by "La Mollura" the unknown writer of the message had meant Molly Sanders, a girl of easy virtue who was a sort of "college widow" with the ranchers of the La Joya region. Intrigues and quarrels over her were frequent, but this looked like murder, for Da Vega was a chivalrous though distant admirer of Molly, and had been known to resent the general slurs cast upon her by various men.

Accordingly the State police obtained from the county engineer a rough map of the region, and the speed of the river current on the east side. This was found to be six miles an hour. The engineer said that the river was without snags or impediments on the east bank for a distance of eleven miles.

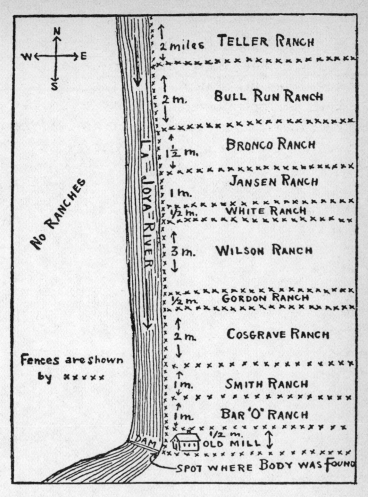

Rough map of La Joya River region furnished to the State police by the county engineer

Had you been a detective, on which ranch would you have said that Portos da Vega probably met his death?

The question to be answered is:

To which ranch would you have directed the search for further clues? (Credit 10.)

Credit Score:

No. 20

THE DUVENANT KIDNAPPING
CASE

Richard Duvenant brought suit for divorce against his wife, the former Dorothy Willington, in 1924, naming as co-respondent an Italian count. It will be remembered that Duvenant won his suit and received from the court the custody of the two children, Fletcher, eight, and Jonathan, four, in spite of their mother's frantic battle to keep at least one of them. This was in May, 1924. The aftermath of the suit, the kidnapping of Jonathan, the younger child, came two months later. Since news of the kidnapping has never yet been published, and since the affair involved a remarkable piece of deduction by one of the Duvenant private detectives, the details are here recounted for the first time.

After the divorce Duvenant continued to live at his country place, The Cedars, near Guildford, going up to the City daily by train. Early in the afternoon of July 14th he received a telephone call from Mlle. Dubois, French governess to his children, who was in charge of them at The Cedars. She was almost incoherent in her terrified announcement that the two boys had both disappeared while playing in the grounds of the estate twenty minutes before. Chauffeur, gardener, and all other servants were engaged in a frantic search of the countryside. Duvenant ordered that the police be notified, and said that he was starting home at once. He then telephoned to the firm of private detectives he had previously employed in the matter of his divorce, and requested that their best man should be rushed to his home by car. Duvenant reached home a little after three and found John Norcross, the head of the firm, already in charge of the investigations on the grounds. Fletcher, the elder boy, had been found by the gardener, but Jonathan, his mother's favourite, was missing. Fletcher told the following story.

He and Jonathan had been playing Indians, and he was hiding in ambush in the tool-house while Jonathan was to ride up on his velocipede and be attacked and scalped. He had waited a long time in the back of the tool-house, from which point he could see nothing outside, and

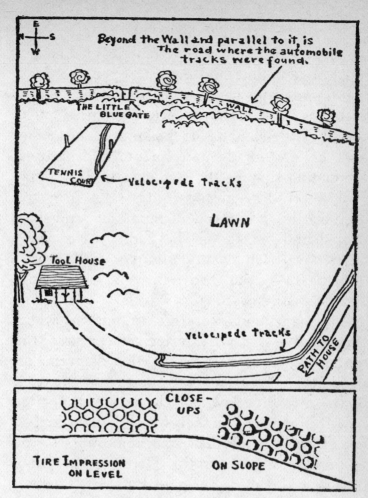

Diagram of the back lawn of the Duvenant estate and close-ups
of tyre impressions on the road

when Jackie did not arrive to be scalped he had tired of the game and gone to open the door. He found it locked. The tool-house locked with a padlock on the outside. Fletcher thought that the little chap had locked him in for a joke, and, therefore, made no noise for some minutes, pretending that he did not care in order that Jackie would be disappointed. But in a few minutes he had grown impatient and had wailed and kicked on the door. After what must have been twenty minutes, his screams were heard by the gardener, who was passing, and he was released.

Duvenant and Norcross found the wheel tracks of Jonathan's velocipede across the tennis-court, as shown on the diagram on page 131. The trail led to the gate at the back of the extensive lawn of the estate, the same " little blue gate," in fact, which had figured so prominently in the newspaper accounts of the Duvenant divorce trial. Deep in the thick bushes to the left of the gate Jonathan's velocipede was found. The footprints of a woman and the footprints of Jonathan leading out of the little gate were found. The gate was locked. On the soft road on which the Duvenant estate backed were found the clearly defined tyre impressions of a large motor-car. There could be no doubt that Jonathan had been persuaded into the car and that it had disappeared, bearing him away. Neither could there be any doubt in Duvenant's mind that his divorced wife had done the deed. Whoever had fetched the child had had a key to the Yale lock which prevented the casual passer-by from opening the gate. White with anger, Duvenant swore to pursue the kidnapper and retrieve the child. His magnificent Fiat car was prepared for the pursuit. But which way had the kidnapper gone, north or south? The road along which the car had travelled ran up a fairly steep slope for 200 yards to the little blue gate, and then ran level. Norcross and Duvenant inspected the tyre tracks closely. Duvenant said that there was nothing to tell whether the kidnapping car had approached from the south and gone north, or vice versa, for the track passed without turning.

This point happened to be of the greatest importance, for the road led north direct towards London and south towards Southampton. It was a Friday, and Duvenant feared that his former wife might be planning to leave the country that night by one of the Friday midnight steamers for New York. A northward journey, on the other hand, probably meant a journey to her father's estate in York-shire, where concealment of the child would be easy.   In either case, to head off or overtake the kidnappers was highly desirable in order to avoid recourse to the law.   Which way had the car gone—north or south?

Norcross rose to the occasion and deduced it from an examination of the car tracks.   Had you been confronted with such a problem, what would you have said?

The questions to be answered are:

1. *In which direction did the kidnapper's car depart from the little blue gate—to the north or to the south?*   (Credit 3.)

2. *What* proved *the direction taken by the car?*   (Credit 7.)

Credit Score:

THE LIGHTHOUSE TRAGEDY AT DEAD MAN'S HARBOUR

At Dead Man's Harbour on the Bay of Fundy there is an isolated village with a population of not more than two hundred persons. At high tide the village is based upon a rocky peninsula which rises sheer twenty feet above the water.

But when the great forty-foot tide rushes out, it leaves the village on a promontory sixty feet in the air; while the island of the lighthouse, almost circular in shape, rises like a great, squat cylinder, nearly forty-three feet above the flat sands.

At ebb tide, for the space of forty minutes, it is possible to cross dry-shod from village to island. Reeled wire ladders, let down the rock, permit descent from the village to the sands below. One can cross to the island and ascend by similar means the almost perpendicular sides of the rock where a level green lawn surrounds the old lighthouse.

The island in Dead Man's Harbour is lonely enough when surrounded by the whipping waters of the bay, but when the cruel rocks rise steeply from the wet sands below it is grim indeed.

On the night of the strange disappearance of Captain Ebenezer Williams, veteran keeper of the lighthouse, high tide came at 11.51, long after Daniel Cobb, the captain's helper, had gone to his home in the village. A heavy fog had settled on the harbour just before eleven o'clock, and the weird moan of the foghorn broke the night with a dismal regularity.

The following morning Daniel Cobb, coming soon after low tide, as was his custom, to relieve the captain, climbed down the ladder on the face of the cliff to cross the sands to the light-house. He noticed a broad trail in the hard-packed, damp sand—as though a board some fifteen inches wide had been dragged over the surface. The impression, Cobb said, was not deep. The board, if it were a board, seemed to have been dragged rather lightly over the sand. The trail ran from the foot of the ladder at the cliff straight to the cliffs of the lighthouse island.

Cobb entered the lighthouse at 6.01 a.m. He called to the captain and started upstairs.

There was no answer. He went to look for him. The captain was not in the lighthouse, nor anywhere on the tiny island. Mystified, Cobb ran to the little boathouse expecting to find the captain's boat gone, only to discover the boat stored away with the oars in their usual place, all dry. The island is less than ninety yards in diameter and is covered with a close-cropped lawn. There was no other place for anyone to hide!

Cobb shouted everywhere and searched diligently in every conceivable place, but there was no trace of Captain Williams. Cobb, it may be stated, was promptly and justifiably exonerated of all suspicion by the examining police; he was of excellent character and deeply attached to the captain.

Cobb then rushed to the edge of the island and peered down the steep sides, but nowhere on the smooth rocks or on the tell-tale expanse of wet sand which surrounded the island completely were any traces whatever except for the fifteen-inch-wide trail which he had observed before reaching the island.

Cobb summoned aid from the village, and searching parties were sent out, since it was unprecedented for the captain to have left the lighthouse untended. The local constable, with

Cobb and several villagers, made a thorough examination of the island and the lighthouse. They could find no trace from which a struggle or foul play could be deduced. They remarked that the foghorn was still blowing, although the fog had lifted that morning a few minutes before low tide. The engine of the foghorn, which had to be refuelled every two hours, still had enough petrol on hand at 6.05 a.m. (when Cobb examined it) to last for nearly another hour.

By 6.20 a.m. the tide was beginning to wash in in earnest. The entire party, therefore, made a minute examination of the single trail to ascertain whether there were any footprints near it. None could be found. Hours went by. It was a mystery—inexplicable, baffling, and to some of the superstitious sailors and fishermen of the village, terrifying. The captain, although he was not a popular man and led an existence much aloof from the villagers, was not known to have any enemies; while no one knew much of his former life, he had been a respected member of the community for eleven years. Where had he gone? The villagers even went to such lengths as to inspect carefully the soil and sod of the island to see if a body might have been cleverly concealed; but there were no traces. Nor could anyone be

The promontory and the lighthouse island at low tide

The promontory and the lighthouse island at high tide

139

found to defend the theory that the captain, strictly devoted to his governmental duty, could have suddenly decided to abandon his post without explanation. Assuming that there had been foul play, it was highly improbable that the murderer, having dragged his victim's corpse across to the cliff base, would have carried it up the ladder and through the single street of the village, as he would have to do to reach the wooded portions of the promontory. Search everywhere in the neighbourhood proved fruitless.

Now it happened that a former official of the French Sûreté Générale, the Scotland Yard of France, was visiting at one of the summer homes in the vicinity—M. Eugène Jacques, who is credited with the solution of the celebrated D'Ormes case of Marseilles. Having heard of the strange disappearance of the captain, he came to the island. Delighted at the interest of so celebrated a detective, the constable requested him to examine the scene and the witnesses, and to pronounce an opinion on the mystery. After a half-hour examination had yielded the facts which have been stated, and after familiarising himself with the locale of the mystery, the French detective startled everyone by pronouncing it a case of cold-blooded murder. "Murder," M. Jacques stated, with the greatest confidence, " by someone who had planned the crime most carefully." The foreigner even predicted the circumstances under which the body of the captain would be found, and with remarkable astuteness reconstructed many of the events of the tragedy.

Two weeks later his predictions concerning the finding of the body proved correct. The mysterious assailant of the captain was subsequently captured, although this was more the result of extreme good luck on the part of the Pennsylvania police than anything else.

The questions to be answered are:

1. *How did M. Jacques know that it was murder?* (Credit 1.)

2. *How did the murderer probably reach the island?* (Credit 2.)

3. *How did he dispose of the body of Captain Williams?* (Credit 2.)

4. *How did he escape from the island?* (Credit 3.)

5. *Under what circumstances would the captain's body probably be found?* (Credit 2.)

Credit Score:

No. 22

WHO MURDERED ALGERNON ASHE?

In crime detection the seemingly insignificant clue often proves to be of the greatest importance. Such a clue ultimately led to the capture of the murderer of Algernon Ashe. Had you been there as detective, what would you have deduced?

The body of Algernon Ashe was found soon after dawn one morning in late July, 1926, in the shrubbery of the beautiful gardens not far from the Monte Carlo Casino. Ashe was an Englishman, a professional gambler and something of a Lothario. He had been stopping at a prominent Monte Carlo hotel for several weeks.

The *gendarmes* who discovered the body noted the following facts. Ashe had been killed by a pistol bullet through the heart, shot from behind. Death had been almost instantaneous. There were no powder marks on the clothes. The pockets of the coat and trousers obviously had been searched, but a large sum of cash and a valuable gold watch had been left. No weapon was found. The man had been dead, they established, at least six hours.

Many footprints, all of them fitting the victim's shoes, indicated that Ashe had walked up and down before a large bush, as if waiting for someone. Two cigarette stubs found in the grass near by bore out the theory of his having waited, for they were of the same distinctive English brand as those in his cigarette-case. Evidently he had waited some time.

A careful search of the entire region of the crime scene revealed the following clues: one burned match; one flat paper match-container (*empty*) of a common French type; one fragment of soft, thin cardboard, partially burned. Printing in English on both sides of the fragment was legible. Both sides of the fragment are reproduced on the next page.

Detectives assigned to the case shrewdly deduced that these had been left by the murderer. Ashe probably had not used the match to light a cigarette because a well-worn patent lighter was found in his vest pocket. The previous night had been an unusually dark one, and a light would have been almost essential to a quick search of pockets. The detectives reasoned that the murderer had struck his last match to make the search, had not finished when the match had burned well down, and had then improvised another match from a bit of cardboard—lighting it from the

match. The match was burned down to an eighth of an inch. But a whole inch of the cardboard fragment remained unburned.

Where had the cardboard come from? Had the murderer, in his haste to find something to ignite before his last match went out, taken it from his own pocket? Probably so, the detectives reasoned, for a man in the murderer's predicament might be expected to seize the first available bit of paper, provided it was not a valuable paper. The fact that he had discarded it when through indicated that it was not valuable to him; further, that he never considered it a dangerous clue.

Puzzling over the meaning of the fragment, of which they could make nothing, the detectives went to the hotel where Ashe had stayed. They found there a letter for the victim. It had come in the early mail. The postmark proved it had been mailed sometime before eleven of the night before in Monte Carlo. Hastily scrawled in a woman's hand, it ran:

A. dearest!

At the last minute I cannot come! I am desolated but it cannot be helped. For some reason he left the tables early and has just told me to pack at once. We leave in an hour. It is the bank stock matter. But I will be back in four days at the most and then India, or Brazil, or anywhere, A. darling, with you. Not more than five days at the most. Will try to get this to you by messenger if it doesn't seem dangerous. If so, will mail. I love you.

Yours forever,

M.

The detectives set about their difficult task of tracing a woman whose name or nickname might begin with M.—whose male escort had hurried her off to somewhere the night before— who wrote English. But the traffic out of

Monte Carlo each day was enormous. Which of the hundreds of departing visitors was she and where had she gone? Examination of many hotel records and the departure records kept by the police yielded no conclusive information on the identity of the woman who had penned the note. Out of hundreds the detectives settled on three parties of travellers as suspects:

MAUDE RHONDA and HOLMHURST RHONDA, daughter and father, of London; departed for Spain.

MARY FREEMAN and FREDERIC FREEMAN, wife and husband, of Buffalo, N.Y.; departed for Paris.

MIRIAM DE RUYTER, LOUISA DE RUYTER, ANDREAS DE RUYTER and SIMON DE RUYTER, two sisters and their brother and father, of Rotterdam, Holland; departed for Rome.

All had departed the previous night. Inquiry at the various hotels where they had stopped yielded no conclusive clues. The De Ruyter family, like most educated Dutchmen, spoke English perfectly. It was ascertained that the father was old and feeble and had been confined to his room that evening until departing. The brother, however, described as a dapper stripling by hotel servants, had been at the casino and had returned early, telling a servant that he had been unlucky again. After visiting the family's apartment he had again gone out. Nothing else could be learned.

Information about the Rhondas and the Freemans was even more difficult to obtain. Attendants at their hotel described Maude Rhonda as beautiful, statuesque, quiet; her father as " stern and even grim, a short, slight man who limped in the left leg, with grey moustache and hair." The Freemans were well-dressed young Americans, apparently with money. Neither had attracted special attention at their hotel. The wife was described as pretty, bright, and petite; the husband as quiet, self-contained — " a tall, stout man, smooth-shaven." Both Freemans were in their early twenties. Nothing could be learned of the movements of the Rhondas or Freemans prior to their departure.

The detectives were in a quandary. Their investigation had yielded nothing to go on. Should they follow all three suspected parties to their destinations? Two of them would prove wild-goose chases, and much time would be lost. They must narrow down the search. This they did by seeking the advice of a famous detective who had travelled widely both in England and America. From the data you now have had he deduced which of the three parties contained the murderer. The detectives followed his advice and ultimately captured their man. The prisoner broke down when his actions at the scene of the crime were reconstructed before him by the detectives, and he later confessed the murder of Ashe.

Which party would you have followed? The questions to be answered are:

1. *Who murdered Algernon Ashe?* (Credit 1.)

2. *How did the detective deduce it?* (Credit 9.)

Credit Score:

EDOUARD TRIMPI'S PERPLEXING DISPATCH

What did Trimpi's dispatch mean and why was he arrested? Baffling at first glance, it is really a simple problem.

At 9.30 on the morning of April 13th the cable editor of the New York *Evening Chronicle* was surprised to receive a cablegram from Barcelona, Spain, evidently sent by Edouard Trimpi, the *Chronicle's* celebrated Paris correspondent, then on sick leave in Spain.

It is reproduced here:

> *Barcelona Apr* 12
> *Press Collect*

Newchron
[New York Chronicle, New York.]
Edouard Ego, regarded as thoroughly competent financial observer, today granted me following interview: " Complete market overturn is imminent on account of accumulated

lack of popular buying of chair shares plus sharp rise steel. Latter bounded today cornering several hundred operators who were seeking to check chair share decline. Such seems impossible because curb buying today with steel as favourite was tumultuous." Another interview promised tomorrow.

Trimpi.

Had Trimpi sent the dispatch? Nothing was expected from him. His regular post was in Paris and his presence in Spain on sick leave a mere matter of chance. He was not a financial expert. The *Chronicle's* regular Spanish correspondent was in Madrid, in another part of Spain. Nothing had come from him for a week; but the news out of Spain was not frequent.

The editors checked back on the cable company and found that the dispatch had been correctly transmitted. Since they had no pre-arranged code with their correspondents several of the editors reached the conclusion that someone was playing a joke.

Others dissented. While debating the matter, the *Chronicle* received a wire from the State Department in Washington, informing it of the bare fact that Trimpi had been taken into custody by the Spanish authorities and was being held incommunicado. This information had been transmitted to the department by the Spanish Ambassador without explanation.

The *Chronicle* made a scoop. What would you have deduced from the situation?

The questions to be answered are:

1. *What had Trimpi done that caused his arrest?* (Credit 5.)

2. *What was the gist of the " Chronicle's" scoop?* (Credit 5.)

Credit Score:

THE CLUB CAR MYSTERY
AT SYRACUSE

There are times in the solution of practical mysteries when quick thinking is essential. Only the failure to think and act quickly in the celebrated Cleveland-New York express train affair (on the part of the detectives in that case) is responsible for the incident going down in history as an unsolved mystery. At least, that is the opinion of Captain McCumber, of the Syracuse Police, who furnishes the following facts established by that ill-managed investigation, to which, unfortunately, he was summoned so late.

The Cleveland-New York express on the night of March 23rd, 1925, was fifteen minutes late on its run from Rochester east into Syracuse. It was, therefore, speeding to make up time. There were unusually few passengers aboard. At the last call for dinner, which was made by a dining-car waiter at 7.40, the club car on the rear end of the train was virtually, if not entirely, deserted by passengers for the diner forward. There was no specific testimony on this point from anyone in the entire course of the investigation.

Smoking is not allowed on long-distance American trains. At the tail end there are two special compartments. The last compartment is called an observation car, and is exactly in the place where the guard's van is on English trains. There is a small platform jutting out at the tail of the train with a few seats on it, protected by a rail, and on these passengers may sit and " observe " the scenery.

Next up the train comes the club car, which is reserved exclusively for men; this and the wash-rooms are the only parts of the train where one may smoke. Adjoining this are the men's washing-rooms and lavatories — the ladies' ditto are usually further up the train. Usually the club car is full of men in shirt-sleeves smoking and playing cards. They also sit round and discuss each other's business, and tell each other all about their wives and other people's wives.

At about 7.50 William Osborne, a realtor of Cleveland, passenger on the train, finished his dinner and returned to the club car, where he had spent the afternoon, to smoke a cigar. Osborne's testimony, subsequently given to the detectives, was as follows:

" I tried the door leading into the club car, and it was locked. I banged on the door, hoping to attract the porter's attention; then I saw a bell near the door and rang that hard several times. Then I pounded loud. Pretty soon the brakeman, or maybe it was one of the conductors, peeked out from behind the curtain of the window in the door, and then he opened the door a little bit. I don't remember what he looked like, only that he was white, not a negro, and he was in uniform.

" ' Car is closed,' he said; ' something's the matter with this car—just wait a few minutes until we get it fixed.'

" ' All right,' I said, as he was starting to close the door on me, ' but please give me the right railroad time, will you? My watch has stopped.'

" I noticed he was kind of impatient, but he pulled out his watch and said:

" ' Eight of eight.'

" I set my watch and turned back, and I guess he locked the door again, but I didn't notice. I never thought anything of it. Then

I went back in the next Pullman in front and sat down."

Asked by a detective: " Are you sure he said ' eight of eight?' " Osborne replied in the affirmative. He remembered it distinctly, he said, because the repetition struck his ear.

According to further testimony of Osborne, approximately two or three minutes later the train slowed down perceptibly on approaching the railroad yard at Syracuse, and a minute or so later had slackened its speed even more as it entered the yards.

At 7.55 Pullman Conductor Yeats and Train Conductor Sedgwick, who had been chatting with passengers forward since 7.30, passed through the train toward the rear and were surprised to discover the club car locked. Thinking that the Pullman porter possibly was taking an opportunity to serve liquor to passengers on the sly, the Pullman conductor opened the door with his key and strode forward with a rebuke on his lips. He stumbled over the crumpled figure of Arthur Johnson, the coloured porter, whose head was bleeding from a cut at the back. The porter was unconscious on the floor near the door. He did not respond to ice water dashed in his face.

The conductors rushed forward. To their

amazement the club car was deserted. Not a person was to be seen. They hurried to the back platform in search of Dennis Sloan, the brakeman. But Sloan was not there as he should have been.

Had he fallen off? Both conductors strained their eyes back over the receding tracks, but could discern no trace of anyone having fallen off the train. They rushed through the train searching for Sloan everywhere. He was not on the train. Even the car roofs were searched in vain.

When Pullman Conductor Yeats had first entered the car and discovered the unconscious porter, Train Conductor Sedgwick had examined the lavatory at the front end of the club car and found it empty. Indeed, all facts of the investigation subsequently established that no one had left the club car *after* the two conductors had entered it.

The conductors were at an absolute loss to explain the situation. Sloan, the young brakeman, had been a trustworthy and exemplary employee for more than three years. Had he and the porter quarrelled? Had they come to blows, and had Sloan fled upon discovering that a blow had rendered the porter unconscious? They had been, apparently, on most amicable terms during the afternoon. Why had the brakeman deserted his post? No attempt had been made to rob the porter of money, but his keys were missing.

As the train pulled into the Syracuse station, Pullman Conductor Yeats discovered the missing brakeman's visored cap and blue-cloth, brass-buttoned coat, neatly rolled into a ball, jammed into the drawer of the writing desk at the rear end of the club car!

The city detective on duty in the station conferred with the conductors. William Osborne, the passenger, heard of the excitement and came forward then with his testimony.

It was at this juncture that the stationmaster hurried up with a telegram just received from the railroad's agent at Ford's Crossing, a hamlet twelve miles west of Syracuse on the railroad line. It said:

Westbound Number 47 stopped one-quarter mile west of here to avoid running over body on westbound tracks. Man dead. Revolver bullet hole behind left ear. Description, six feet one, about two hundred pounds, age about sixty, grey moustache, well dressed, brown tweed suit, wallet containing three hundred fifty dollars and commutation ticket Long

Island Railroad between Hempstead and New York City, in name of Anthony Capewell. Wallet initials J. A. C. Was he dropped from Number Thirty-one? Local constable in charge. Instruct me.

Murtree, Agent.

Train Number 31 was the Cleveland-New York express.

You have now all the facts of the mystery which confronted the detectives in the Syracuse station upon the arrival of the train.

None of the passengers or train crew could add anything to the meagre data available. Doctors in care of Johnson, the Pullman porter, feared that he might not regain consciousness for several hours. Yet the need for immediate action was obvious.

Suppose you had been in charge of the investigation—what would you have deduced about the mystery? How would you have reasoned and acted in the emergency?

These are the questions to be answered:

1. *What would you have done to locate Dennis Sloan, the brakeman?* (Credit 3.)

2. *Would you have ordered the arrest of*

Dennis Sloan, the brakeman, on a charge of murder of Capewell?   (Credit 2.)

3. *Would you have ordered his arrest as an accomplice?*   (Credit 1.)

4. *Was Sloan guilty of assault on the porter?* (Credit 2.)

5. *What in all probability happened in the club car after the last call to dinner?* (Credit 2.)

Credit Score:

No. 25

THE MYSTERY OF HAJI LAL DEB

No land offers more bizarre and ingenious crimes and concealments of crimes than India. Naturally subtle, the Oriental mind, when it does turn to crime, manages sometimes to baffle the authorities rather neatly. Until as late as 1820 British rule in India had not become adept in fighting the elaborate system of highway robbery, gang thieving (dacoity), and professional poisoning which had been spreading virtually unchecked for many years. British detectives in the Indian service were confronted with strange conditions among strange peoples. Gradually they learned how to cope with Indian crime.

The following problem in crime detection is based on an extract from the case book of Deputy Superintendent Hardesty Mainwaring, of the Bombay district, who later rose to head the Metropolitan Police of London. In his Looking Backward (*Methuen, London,*

1905), the famous investigator writes:

"Late in the summer of 1879, shortly after my first colonial appointment, I was requested by the native officer at Bunoorah to advise on a baffling case which was arousing considerable excitement in that village.

"Some ten days previously a well-to-do merchant of the village had vanished mysteriously one night when he was known to be carrying a sizeable sum in rupees. No word having come from him the morning after his disappearance, the merchant's widow had raised a hue and cry with the local authorities. There was some reason to suspect that the man had been done away with, for murder to gain a few rupees was common enough at that time —and the merchant was a tempting bait to the professional poisoners operating in the district.

"Among others upon whom a certain measure of suspicion rested was a former servant in the household of the merchant, one Haji Lal Deb. Several months previously he had been discharged on suspicion of stealing foodstuffs, and although the authorities had nothing definite to go on they instinctively had reached the conclusion that Haji Lal Deb knew something of the matter.

"However, 'knowing' and 'proving' in

India are two very different things. The former servant was a stone wall when it came to giving information as to the whereabouts of the merchant. He convinced the native officer that he had not the slightest idea of what could have happened in the affair. No less than seven relatives and friends staunchly supported his statements, and nothing came of the questioning. Nor were the authorities more successful in their quest at other sources.

" But on the day of my arrival at Bunoorah —some two weeks after the disappearance—a native woman of the village came to the local investigating officer with the following story. She assigned as her reason for not having come sooner that she had been ill and had heard nothing of the gossip of the disappearance.

"Very early in the morning of the day following the disappearance of the merchant, she recalled, she had encountered Haji Lal Deb walking rapidly away from a certain isolated district on the outskirts of the town *carrying a spade over his shoulder*. She was in a hurry herself to visit her brother, who was ill of the plague then afflicting the district, and had thought nothing of the incident. Haji Lal Deb, she remembered, was walking toward his hut, which was itself on the outskirts of the village.

" With something of a gleam of triumph in our eyes, the local investigating officer and I proceeded immediately to the hut, and there found Haji Lal Deb—as calm, impassive, and innocent looking an old native as you could imagine.

" To our amazement he admitted readily enough that he had been walking in the spot described at the time described, and carrying a spade. But he knew nothing of the rich merchant, said he; he had been engaged on the sad errand of burying his wife's cousin, an aged man who had died of the plague the night previous. And would Sahib not believe him? Come, he would show Sahib the very grave.

" Now it was perfectly true that the fellow might be telling the truth. The natives had been dying off like flies at this time, and there was nothing unusual about a hurried burial of a body, under the emergency conditions then obtaining. Indeed, to prevent spread of the disease, prompt burial would have been essential. The native officer recalled the report that a relative in the house of Haji Lal Deb had died about the time of the disappearance of the merchant, and he duly noted that the household had engaged in observance of suitable rites of mourning.

" However, it seemed the part of prudence to check the story, and accordingly we allowed Haji Lal Deb to lead us to the spot where the aged relative had been buried. To our astonishment—for I had come to suspect the fellow—our spadesmen had not dug more than three feet down when we came upon the body of an aged native. Most evidently he had died of the plague, and there could be no mistaking that it was the corpse of an old, emaciated man, whereas, the missing merchant had been a stout fellow in the prime of life.

" I had never felt more ' sold ' in my life. The local officer and I were indeed so moved that we pressed a few rupees on Haji Lal Deb, and with some words of apology retired to seek solution of the mystery elsewhere.

" There were some trifling clues which we thought might lead somewhere along other trails, and we were engaged in sifting these in their possible relation to other suspects, when suddenly we received a bit of information which I recognized as of the greatest importance. It was given to us by the son of a neighbour of Haji Lal Deb, who happened to overhear us lamenting the fruitlessness of our expedition of the morning.

" The aged cousin of the wife of Haji Lal

Deb, we learned, had died the day *before* the disappearance of the merchant, not *on* the night of the disappearance. . . ."

How Deputy-Superintendent Mainwaring solved the mystery and fastened the guilt upon Haji Lal Deb is one of the classics of crime detection in the Bombay district.

The questions to be answered are:

1. *Why did Mainwaring suspect that Haji was guilty?* (Credit 4.)

2. *By what step did he prove the guilt?* (Credit 6.)

Credit Score:

THE STRANGE CASE OF THE PROMISSORY NOTE

When Richard Mannington died in 1902 he left to his widow a fortune of £ 500,000 and his famous collection of porcelains. Scarcely ten days after Mannington's death the widow received a bombshell in the form of the following letter from one Philip Rannard, of Hartingdon Manor, near Birmingham.

At this time of your sorrow, I hesitate to speak of a matter which goes back more than twenty years, when your late husband and I had our unfortunate disagreement over the Ming vase, of the details of which you are undoubtedly to some extent aware. I had thought never to be obliged to advance my claim, but circumstances now compel it in justice to myself and others.

In June, 1882, I had just returned from a five years' stay in China, when I became acquainted with your husband at the home of the Levericks in Berkeley Square. I had brought with me seventeen pieces, including the two vases of the Ming Dynasty, which to-day form the basis of your late husband's celebrated collection. Mannington was at that time interested more as a speculator, attracted by the chance of profit in the purchase and sale of Chinese art, than he was in collecting for art's sake. To make a long story short, he purchased from me at that time the pieces enumerated upon the separate memorandum, and at the prices named. He paid me then, according to our agreement, £1,000 in cash, and gave me his promissory note for £6,000, £7,000 being the total amount of the transaction.

It is one of the regrets of my life that out of this transaction grew the serious misunderstanding between us which resulted a year later in a rupture of our friendly relations. You probably are aware that soon after the making of our agreement several experts, undoubtedly bribed by envious dealers, declared the vases counterfeit. Your husband ultimately refused point-blank to pay his note.

Perhaps you are " not " aware that after violent disputes on the matter the authenticity of the pieces was established beyond a doubt only six months ago. Until this had occurred I did not care to press my claim against your husband, although personally I had never doubted that the vases were genuine. I had written several times to your husband since then but received no reply whatever. Three months ago I was on the point of bringing suit against him when I was taken seriously ill, an illness from which I have only just recovered.

I repeat that it gives me pain to force the issue at this time, but circumstances compel me to do so. I am sure we both wish to avoid the unpleasantness of a suit, and I have determined to throw myself upon your sense of justice, even though the technicalities of the law might seem to make recognition of the debt unlikely in view of the lapse of years.

I enclose a photographic copy of your husband's note. The original is in the possession of my solicitors, McArthur, Long & McArthur, of Lincoln's Inn, from whom any further details may be had. I trust, however, that we may settle the matter between ourselves rather than between attorneys.

Mrs. Mannington had been married to her husband for only ten years. He was a man who had never discussed business matters with his wife, and she could neither deny nor affirm the justice of the claim. The note, according to what was said to be a photograph of it, bore Mannington's distinctive signature. The formal text of the note, duly couched in the correct legal language, was typewritten. It was turned over to handwriting and typewriting experts, who pronounced it authentic. The handwriting experts, and some of Mannington's old friends, advised the widow that the signature was not only undoubtedly that of Mannington but that it was characteristic of Mannington's signature at that particular period of his life. And the typewriting experts pronounced the type characteristic of the machines used in the early 'eighties.

No record of the transaction could be found in the papers of the deceased, but the details regarding the authentication of the Ming jars proved to be true. A complete report of the authentication had recently been published by the *Ceramics Journal*. Of Philip Rannard, the claimant, Mrs. Mannington knew only that he had indeed been an old friend of her late husband, and that Rannard was the brother of Adela Rannard, now deceased, who had been a sweetheart of Mannington in the early 'eighties. It was known that Adela Rannard and Mannington had once carried on an extensive correspondence.

This was not the first time that Mrs. Mannington's faith in her late husband's integrity had been disturbed. Before her marriage she had heard ugly gossip of the methods by which he had gained his fortune. She knew that throughout her married life he had been almost jealously devoted to his valuable collection. Had he in his earlier years stooped to dishonesty in assembling it? To her any threat of stain on her dead husband's reputation was terrifying. Anxious to avoid publicity she directed her solicitor to accompany her to Lincoln's Inn to examine the original document and settle the matter at once.

At the ensuing conference, for which Rannard came up to town, Mrs. Mannington and her solicitor were favourably impressed by the claimant. Philip Rannard was a large, suave, courtly gentleman, apparently of the greatest sincerity. His solicitors were among the best known in London, and had been established for years. The original note, slightly yellowed with age, was produced. Mrs. Mannington and her lawyer compared it carefully with the photograph which had been sent to them. They were obviously identical.

Anxious to settle the matter and feeling financially able to do so, the widow announced frankly her willingness to take up the note. Everyone was pleased. The lady was about to draw the cheque, and the lawyers were congratulating each other upon the happy settlement of the affair, when suddenly Mrs. Mannington's eyes fell upon the back of the note which bore her husband's signature.

She paused and asked to examine the document again. Rannard's lawyer handed it to her.

It was about six inches wide and a little less from top to bottom. Mannington's signature, directly under the typed lines of the promise to pay, fell in the centre of the paper (from side to side), a quarter of an inch above the bottom edge of the paper.

Turning the note over, Mrs. Mannington examined what had caught her eye on the back. This is what she saw along the bottom margin in a spot almost conciding with the signature on the reverse of the sheet:

These lines, obviously made by pen and ink,

were the only markings on the back of the note.

Mrs. Mannington looked at them carelessly and handed the note back. She then said that she had not brought the right cheque book with her and would have to return to her house and get it. She departed with her lawyer at 5 p.m. But she never returned.

Early that evening Mrs. Mannington's solicitor called hastily on Mr. McArthur, senior member of the firm of lawyers representing Rannard, and warned him that Philip Rannard was in all probability a clever crook. Shocked, Mr. McArthur demanded the reasons for the charge, and when he heard them he paused in dismay. In the presence of the Mannington lawyer he telephoned to Rannard's hotel.

"Mr. Rannard was called out of town suddenly just before dinner," he was informed by the hotel clerk.

And Mrs. Mannington never heard of Philip Rannard again.

What had aroused Mrs. Mannington's suspicions and what had Rannard done? Had you been a detective assigned to the case, what would you have made of the mystery?

The questions to be answered are:

1. *Why did the strange markings on the back of the yellowed document lead Mrs. Manning-*

ton to suspect that something might be wrong?
(Credit 3.)

2. *Where had Rannard probably obtained
the piece of paper which bore Mannington's
signature?* (Credit 7.)

Credit Score:

No. 27

THE DEATH OF BARNABAS FROBISHER

Barnabas Frobisher, retired City magnate, was found dead in his library, a bullet through his head. Had a crime been committed? If so, by whom and how? Answers to these questions can be deduced from the following established facts and the official police sketch of the death scene.

At 9.30 on the evening of January 12th the Chislehurst police received a telephone call from a man who spoke in an excited voice:

"This is the butler at Mr. Barnabas Frobisher's. Mr. Frobisher has shot himself. He's just killed himself. I'm all alone in the house. It's terrible. What? Yes—the Kemnal Road. Yes, I'll stay here. Graves—John Graves, the butler."

Bourne Lodge, the house of the Frobishers, like most Chislehurst houses, stood well isolated in its own grounds, and this although it was a small house, the Frobishers being but two in family.

The police found Graves waiting anxiously by the front door. In the library they found Barnabas Frobisher slumped down in an armchair, dead from a bullet which had entered the middle of his forehead. A revolver, later identified as Frobisher's, lay on the seat of the chair between the side of the chair and the left thigh of the dead man, as it might have fallen if it had slipped from his grasp. Below the wound and on the backs of the fingers of both hands were powder marks. On the revolver were faint traces of fingerprints which were later found to be Frobisher's. Only one bullet had been fired from the revolver and it was this bullet which had killed Frobisher. The body had not been robbed.

Frobisher's wife was out at a house called Holm Dene, playing bridge. The cook and the housemaid were out at an entertainment at the Village Hall. They were all summoned by telephone, and pending their arrival the police examined the butler. The butler told the following story:

" It is no secret that Mr. Frobisher has been losing money from speculations lately. He has not been himself. He has quarrelled with his

wife several times in the last few weeks over
what he called her extravagances.   She de-
nounced him for speculating, and they did not
speak to each other for the last twenty minutes
of dinner.

" Mrs. Frobisher went to Holm Dene at 9
o'clock, and Mr. Frobisher went into the library
a couple of minutes later and locked the door
after him, as he usually does.   I took him his
port as soon as I went in, and I came right out.
Then I stayed in the pantry and the kitchen
waiting if he should call for anything, and at
about a quarter past nine the cook and housemaid left the kitchen to get ready to go to an
entertainment at the Village Hall that the mistress had said they could attend.   Byles, the
chauffeur, came back for them after leaving
Mrs. Frobisher at Holm Dene.   I heard the car
arrive and the engine was kept running at the
side door till the maids came out and got into
it.   Then Byles drove off with them.   Then it
suddenly occurred to me that maybe Mr. Frobisher had rung and that I hadn't heard it.   The
buzzer sounds in the pantry, and I had been
mostly in the kitchen seeing the maids off.   So
I went into the pantry and knocked on the door
of the library.   There was no answer.   I opened
it a little and I saw him slumped down just as

you found him, with his head all bleeding. I rushed in and felt his pulse and saw he was dead, and went right out without touching a thing, and telephoned to the police station. That is all I know. He must have shot himself while the engine was running and I was in the kitchen and I didn't hear the shot."

Annie O'Hagen, the old and trusted cook of the Frobisher household, had by now arrived with the housemaid, and corroborated the butler's presence in the pantry and kitchen until she and the housemaid left about 9.25. It was established that Frobisher was alive at about 9.15, for before leaving to dress, the cook, stopping in the pantry, heard him cough in the adjacent library, and heard his glass laid down on the little table. The butler, she testified, was at that time in the kitchen. She then went up, put on her outdoor clothes, and went out to the car with the maid.

Was the butler telling the truth? The police examined minutely the highly polished surface of the newly-waxed floor of the library and found there what seemed to be corroboration of his story. Frobisher's heel marks from the door connecting to the hall led to the armchair in which he was found—and ended there. It was established that he customarily went to the

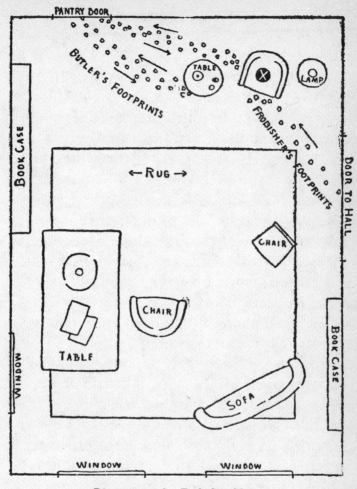

Diagram of the Frobisher library

library after dinner, bolted the door after him to prevent disturbance, and often sat there reading for hours. The door was found bolted by the police.

From the door between pantry and library were two coming and two going sets of heel marks which fitted the butler's shoes. They agreed with his statement of his only two trips into the room: first, to serve the wine; later, to examine the body. Careful examination of the floor revealed no other footprints, but the detectives, by tests, determined that a person might have walked in stockinged feet on the floor without leaving any mark. Only the rubber heels, worn by both Frobisher and the butler, had left prints.

Mrs. Frobisher, arriving on the scene, confirmed the butler's testimony of quarrels over speculation with her husband, but denied vehemently that he would have taken his own life merely on that account or because of losses from speculations. She said she could offer no adequate reason for suicide. On the other hand, she could not suggest why anyone should have desired his death. She testified most positively —and her opinion was shared by the cook— that Frobisher was not the kind of man who would commit suicide. On the other hand, both refused to believe that John Graves, the butler, could have shot Frobisher, for neither knew of any animosity between the two men or any possible motive. Graves had been with the family for over a year.

Investigation revealed that Mrs. Frobisher had been at Holm Dene from 9.10 until summoned home by the tragedy, and that Annie O'Hagen and the housemaid had been at the Village Hall during the time she had said she was there. John Graves, the butler, stoutly denied further knowledge. When asked if he thought it possible that some intruder had entered the house and shot Frobisher while he, Graves, was in the kitchen, the butler denied the possibility. He pointed out that the hall door of the library and all the windows had been locked from the inside. The police had found this to be the case.

You now have all the evidence which was available to the police on the night of the death of Barnabas Frobisher. What do you deduce about the mystery? Three days later much light was shed by the discovery of certain papers in the private files of the dead man, and of these you will read in the Answer Section. Meanwhile, these are the questions to be answered:

1. *At whose hands did Barnabas Frobisher meet his death?* (Credit 5.)

2. *How do you know it?* (Credit 5.)

Credit Score:

No. 28

THE HUPPENHEIMER MUSEUM
ROBBERY

*This is a long and complicated mystery. Read
it carefully*

One Sunday morning, soon after the great
Huppenheimer Museum of Pittsburg had
opened its doors for the day, a guard on the
second floor was startled by a ponderous clank
from a corridor in the Egyptian wing. Thinking that a statue had fallen, he rushed in the
direction of the sound. Instead he saw a man,
who was struggling to replace the heavy lid of
a sarcophagus, suddenly let go of the lid and
dart away. The guard seized his coat collar,
but the fugitive squirmed from his coat, dodged
behind an exhibit case, and vanished. When
the breathless guard arrived downstairs at the
front door he found that the intruder had
walked out quietly and was lost from sight.
The doorman had supposed him a workman of
the museum and had thought nothing of his
departure.

This event brought to the attention of the authorities the singular incident of the museum robbery, which resulted in the great scandal of 1924. Detective Wagner, who was assigned to the case, later summarised the affair as follows:

" I arrived at the museum Monday morning and was ushered into the office of Director Oddie, who had the captured coat on a chair beside him. The doctor told me of the coat incident and then said:

" ' I am sorry to say that this means a clever attempt at a serious robbery. This fellow to whom the coat belongs had undoubtedly managed to stay in the museum overnight. Investigation revealed that our case number 12 had been robbed of its contents in a most ingenious manner. But fortunately the thief has been badly fooled. What he was after, of course, was the Rurik gem collection which Mr. Huppenheimer purchased only last year. What he got was the set of paste replicas which we always keep in the exhibit case except upon occasions when distinguished persons visit us. The real gems are then taken from a safe and temporarily installed in the case. Now, this fellow had cunningly prepared a dummy set of the gems, in their distinctive settings, and had managed to insert them in the case when he extracted what he thought were the real jewels.

" ' In short, we have played a $80,000 joke on the robber. At the same time, I shudder at the ease with which the fellow did his work. It is of the utmost importance, of course, that we track the man down.

" ' This may not be so hard as you think '; Dr. Oddie continued, ' for I learn this morning from Curator Waltham, of the Section of Antique Jewels that the owner of the coat has probably been in the museum frequently in the last few weeks. Three weeks ago to-morrow a man representing himself as Antonio Diaz, a designer of jewellery, applied for permission to make drawings of the Rurik pieces. The copying of designs by the public, you know, is a regular thing with us. We encourage it to aid all the industrial arts and handicrafts. Persons have frequently copied the Rurik designs. They have to do this through the glass of the case, using a magnifying glass.

" ' Our guard is always near the case in the day time. The thief could not have taken the screws out of the case except by night. This he did, removing the paste replicas and substituting the fake pieces which he had made. As you will see, the dummy set is cleverly made. The fellow had not spent his days of copying for nothing. He hoped, of course, to make his way out of the museum in the morning with what he thought was the real set, leaving his dummy set to lull us into continual security.

" ' Indeed, had he not replaced several of the screws crookedly, I doubt if we would have noticed which case had been tampered with. Our night watchman makes the rounds every half hour; the thief must have been hurried as he was finishing his task of screwing up the side of the case. The culprit, I take it, must have hidden in the sarcophagus during the early hours of light Sunday morning, while waiting for the doors to open. He would have escaped without leaving any clue whatever if the guard in the Egyptian wing had not seen him. Probably, while climbing out of the sarcophagus the lid slipped from his grasp. Now the question is: what does this coat tell you?'

" And Dr. Oddie handed it to me.

" I examined the coat and the contents of its pockets, but had to confess to Dr. Oddie that I could make nothing of it. It was an ordinary brown coat of cheviot, well worn. There was no label or identifying mark of any kind. The right-hand pocket yielded a cheap screwdriver and a piece of white string. In the left-hand pocket we found a small gimlet, some rubber bands, and a package of winter-green drops. In the upper left-hand pocket (outside breast) I found two stubs of tickets to a large New York picture theatre—very much frayed, and a bit of white paper about three inches by one. This was not soiled or frayed, as were the ticket stubs. I judged that it was a portion of a roll from an adding machine, for it had printed on it a column of numbers, as if someone had started to add a series of cheques or amount of money. No total, however, was given. It ran thus:

```
12.09
23.22
 9.22
23.13
27.18
15.15
76.22
 8.23
26.28
79.18
16.22
 8.12
12.13
```

" I was about to request Dr. Oddie to take me to case number 12 for a search for finger-prints when the door of the office burst open and a tall, elderly man rushed in on us in the greatest excitement.

"'Doctor!' he cried, 'we have been robbed. It is terrible! The pieces in the safe are *not* the originals! A terrible mistake must have been made, and the thief has taken the *real* gems.'

"It was Curator Waltham, who had just come from the safe where the real jewels supposedly were resting. Dr. Oddie and I were staggered at this turn of events. We hastily plied the curator for details.

"Three weeks ago to the day," Curator Waltham said, " he personally had removed the real gems from the safe and examined them carefully in anticipation of their exhibit to the Prince of Wales, who was to visit the museum that noon. To make way for them he had directed Assistant Curator Raymond to remove the replicas from the case (number 12) and keep them in his desk.

"The curator testified in the most absolute way that he personally had carried the real gems to the case and had installed them there. He remained while the guards locked the case before his eyes, and stood directly by the case awaiting the reception committee and the Prince.

"Only the curator had the key to the lock. He was prepared, if the Prince expressed a desire to handle the famous pieces, to remove them himself and hand them to the Prince. However, the visit was hurried, and the Prince did not make the request.

"Of the subsequent events Curator Waltham said:

"'I remember distinctly that after the Prince left, I left Assistant Curator Raymond in charge to remove the true pieces and put them securely away in the safe, for I was compelled to join the committee accompanying His Highness for the rest of the tour through the museum. I cannot say that I saw Raymond do it, but I am as certain of his honour and integrity as I am of my own. He reported to me only an hour later that he *had* done so, and that the paste replicas had been restored to case number 12.

"'Yet Raymond is so careful, it seems impossible that he could have made any mistake about this. I confess that I am inclined to the belief that this thief whose coat was captured in some way must have obtained the combination of the safe and stolen the real pieces from *it,* also robbing the case of the replicas and putting them in the safe. Thus he hoped that a long time would elapse before the fraud would be discovered in either safe or exhibit case, since our replicas would be in the safe and his dummy set in the case. That would give him more time to sell them without an alarm being spread.'

"Dr. Oddie affirmed in the most positive manner his complete trust in both the Curator and the Assistant Curator. He added that he agreed with Curator Waltham's theory. However, they placed the investigation entirely in my hands and were good enough to express the fullest confidence in me.

"Our first step was to telegraph Mr. Raymond, the Assistant Curator, recalling him immediately from an emergency mission to the New York Metropolitan Museum of Art, on which he had been sent the Friday before. Within a few hours Raymond had wired that he was starting back at once.

"In the meantime I made a searching investigation among this Raymond's friends, and found that he bore a reputation for good character and devotion to the museum. He arrived the next day.

"I would describe him as a scholarly appearing young man in his early thirties, with a frank, open countenance, though highly nervous in his manner. He appeared to be greatly shocked at what had taken place, immediately offered to resign, and courted the fullest investigation.

"He told us convincingly that he personally had removed the jewels from the case. Then, he said, he had put them into the safe and locked it; after which he had carried the replicas from his desk back to case number 12 and inserted them in their proper places. He had personally supervised the locking of the case and examined it to see if it was secured—all before he had gone to luncheon on the day of the visit of the Prince.

"I confess that I was persuaded as to his sincerity and the truth of his story, as were Dr. Oddie and Curator Waltham. I was completely baffled, I had been unable to get any trace of Antonio Diaz (no doubt an alias) and after several days' searching my investigation left me as mystified as ever.

"There were no fingerprints on the case or on the museum safe. None of the guards could shed light on the mystery. I was certain that it was an inside job, but I couldn't lay finger on a person. Only Dr. Oddie, Curator Waltham and Assistant Curator Raymond possessed the combination of the safe which had held the jewels."

Such was Detective Wagner's summary of the case up to the evening of March 3rd. On that evening, as he was sitting in his office in Police Headquarters, re-examining the captured coat and its contents, an idea occurred to him. By dawn he had reached a solution of the mystery.

It was as clever a piece of detective work as the country had seen in twenty years. Before noon of that day a man had been arrested on the charge of robbing the Huppenheimer Museum. Who was that man? How did the detective know it? What would you have deduced?

The questions to be answered are:

1. *How many were guilty in the robbery?* (Credit 2.)

2. *Who?* (Credit 3.)

3. *How was the robbery carried out?* (Credit 2.)

3. *How was the guilt conclusively proved?* (Credit 3.)

Credit Score:

HOGARTH CRIME

Surreptitious slaughter, and the reasons behind it, have never lost their power to enthrall. Old ladies' wills and wilful old ladies, the sleuth in evening dress, the eccentric village squire and the portly butler (who either saw, or did it) continue to exert their fascination.

Some detective stories have worn rather better than others – as a rule, those in which playfulness, assurance and ingenuity are well to the fore.

The Hogarth Crime series, in reviving novels unjustly neglected as well as those by the justly famous, offers a new generation the cream of classic detective fiction from the Golden Age.

Rex Stout

The Hand in the Glove

The plush Manhattan offices of Bonner & Raffray Inc. are a far cry from the dingy quarters of most of New York's private investigators. But then Theodolinda Bonner – known to her closest friends as Dol – is a far from ordinary detective.

Investigating a murder at a swanky New England house party she is attending, Dol's help is much begrudged by the New York Bureau of Homicide. But armed with her Holcomb automatic – and a contempt for the opposite sex of which Sam Spade would have been proud – Dol sets out to beat them all at their own game . . .

Gladys Mitchell
The Saltmarsh Murders

Cosy English villages can be murderously peaceful.

Noel Wells is a young curate in the sleepy village of Saltmarsh. His life passes in helping the Reverend Bedivere Coutts with his sermons and dancing with Daphne to the gramophone in the vicarage study. Then one day Mrs Coutts discovers that her unmarried house-maid is pregnant, and the trouble begins.

Noel knows just the person to help: Mrs Beatrice Adela Lestrange Bradley, beady-eyed guest at the Manor House, who in her unnervingly unorthodox investigation tackles with relish a smuggler, the village lunatic, a missing corpse, a public pillorying, an exhumation and – naturally – a murderer.

'The Great Gladys' – Philip Larkin

Romilly and Katherine John
Death by Request

This morning the usually hearty breakfast at Friars Cross is somewhat subdued, for the sixth member of the party is still upstairs – dead.

Who can possibly be the murderer? Colonel Lawrence is a blundering idiot; Phyllis Winter is of a frail and hysterical disposition; Mrs Fairfax and Judith Grant seem to have no motive; the Barrys all have alibis. So *did* the butler, who has unfortunately embraced socialism, do it? And can a private investigator make a correct deduction when he is in love with one of his suspects?

Death By Request comes straight from the heart of the Golden Age of detective fiction.

Anthony Berkeley
Dead Mrs Stratton

'Give Roger Sheringham his three chief interests in life, and he is perfectly happy – criminology, human nature and good beer.'

At a fancy-dress party Murderers and Victims dance beneath a mock gallows. But the revelry takes a sinister turn as a real victim is discovered, and when the local constabulary declare Sheringham their chief suspect, the case becomes by far the most dangerous of the illustrious detective's career.

Dead Mrs Stratton is one of Anthony Berkeley's most exciting and entertaining novels, and he brings to it all the wit and irony that helped establish his international reputation for original crime writing.

THE BAFFLE BOOK
ANSWER SECTION

ANSWER SECTION

No. 1

WHO MURDERED ELLINGTON BREESE?

1. Walters, the nephew, murdered Ellington Breese. (Credit 5.)

2. The police deduced that Walters was the murderer from the fact that the flies and the mosquitoes found dead were on the window sill instead of around the room. This indicated that the gas had permeated the room *after* dawn, for the following reasons: a poison gas, powerful enough to kill a human being, would kill instantly such insects as flies and mosquitoes. Therefore they must have been at the windows when overtaken by the gas. From this it can be deduced that it was light at the time, since such insects, in a dark room, are attracted to the windows by the light coming in beneath partially drawn blinds. It may be logically considered to be very improbable that

the flies would all have been found on the window sills had the instantaneously fatal gas been released in the darkness of the night. (Credit 5.)

Observation of this clue led the detectives to another questioning of Walters, who eventually broke down and confessed to the crime. He had stolen down at the break of dawn. Desperate losses in wild-cat speculation, it later developed, had driven Walters to the deed. He was subsequently convicted and executed early in 1926.

No. 2

THE EVIDENCE ON THE JAPANNED BOX

1. A guest stole the Elgin emerald from the japanned box which the owner, Stephen Lerian, had left carelessly upon the living-room table. (Credit 5.)

2. The thief was Miss Charlotte Grainger, as indicated by the tell-tale thumbmark on the rim of the inside of the cover of the japanned box. (Credit 5.)

Charlotte Grainger's thumbprint was the only one which was identical in its ridge markings with the thumbprint on the japanned box cover.

The distinctive feature of both prints is the arch formation of the ridges.

The ridges are classified according to types— loops, whorls, arches. For instance Colonel Blue's thumbprint would be classified as distinguished by its whorls; that of Mr. Hay by its loops; and Charlotte Grainger's was the only one distinguished by its arches.

The dangerous aftermath of Stephen Lerian's private investigation into the disappearance of his emerald was no fault of his. The unfortunate girl, whose kleptomaniacal impulses were unknown even to her uncle and aunt, Mr. and Mrs. Archibald Hay, was herself the cause of the unpleasant publicity which the whole case received. Lerian refrained from broaching his shocking discovery to the girl's uncle until she and the Hays had returned to the Hay home. Her uncle decided to search her room. The niece, coming upon her uncle just as he had located the missing jewel in her drawer, flew at him in a desperate assault and seriously injured him with a paper cutter which she had

snatched up. Every effort was made to hush up the affair, but it was revealed to the police through servants who had suffered from the girl's ungovernable bursts of temper. It was this that forced the Hays to agree to her confinement in a private sanatorium. The Hays, it must be recorded, placed no blame whatever upon Lerian for his methods in detecting the theft.

No. 3

THE ELEVATED TRANSIT MYSTERY

Part I

1. The body fell to the pavement under Cho Sing's windows from *the roof of the last car* of the elevated railway train which swung around the curve about 2.28 a.m.   (Credit 4.)

Captain Danforth deduced as follows:
The body was not on the tracks, according to the track walker's testimony, just before the train came to the spot. It had not come from the platforms or windows of the cars of the

train, according to all available testimony of passengers and guards. Upon striking the sidewalk the body had enough impetus or spin in it to roll under an awning attached to the building in which Cho Sing's restaurant was housed. Therefore it was highly probable that the snap of the end car of the train making the curve was the cause of the impetus—an impetus *away* from the path of the train and *toward* the building. While it was *possible* that the body might have been flung from a window above Cho Sing's, or from the roof, on to the car's roof, it was extremely improbable that the murderer would have done so, because Cho Sing's restaurant was open and crowded. To have done so would have invited detection. Therefore, Captain Danforth reasoned, it was almost certain that the murder had occurred uptown somewhere, and that the murderer had thrown the body on the roof of the car to get it carried far from the scene of the crime.

2. The roof of the rear end of the train is what should have been searched particularly for clues which might lead to the apprehension of the murderer. (Credit 1.)

How Captain Danforth did search there and

what he found and deduced therefrom, you will
see in Part II of "The Elevated Transit
Mystery."

PART II

Captain Danforth directed search immediately to the "zone of suspicion" which lay
between One Hundred and Eleventh Street and
the Ninety-ninth Street stations of the Elevated Transit Company's Tenth Avenue line.
(Credit 2.)

Captain Danforth reasoned thus : He eliminated as *improbable* the "zone of suspicion"
nearest the One Hundred and Fifty-first Street
station, in view of the testimony of Inspector
Monahan. (Monahan had said the body was
not on the roof of Train No. 34 when he
watched it pass downtown from the bridge at
the One Hundred and Twentieth Street
station.)

Captain Danforth then eliminated as *impossible* the "zone of suspicion" which centred at
the Seventy-fourth Street station. He did this
because the Weather Bureau report showed
that the shower had burst on the uptown region
at 2.20 a.m., at which time Train No. 34 had
only reached the Ninetieth Street station on its

downtown journey. The roof of the train must have been thoroughly wetted by the time it reached the " zone of suspicion " at Seventy-fourth Street, and if the body had been thrown on in that zone there could not have been a perfectly dry spot apparent on the otherwise soaked roof of the car. But such a dry spot, in the shape of a sprawled body, *had* been found on the roof of the rear-end car. Therefore, Captain Danforth deduced, the body must have been thrown on *before* the shower began. Hence his selection of the " zone of suspicion " which lay between the One Hundred and Eleventh and the Ninety-ninth Street stations, for the train had passed through it *before* the shower had begun.

How the detectives searched in the suspected zone, what they found there, and how Captain Danforth finally located the murder scene and captured the murderer, you will learn in Part III of " The Elevated Transit Mystery."

Part III

1. The building in which the detective found the final clues was that in which the Palace Gardens, a dance hall, was located. (Credit 2.)

2. Captain Danforth deduced that the dance-hall building, rather than any other, was the place of greatest suspicion, thus: the soles of the shoes of the victim had been found dry, not wet; the water which had soaked other parts of his clothing *on the back,* had been warded off the slippery, waxed soles of his shoes, as observed by the police when they first examined him. Almost certainly, then, the man had been dancing just previous to his death, and this pointed to the Palace Gardens. (Credit 1.)

Captain Danforth, after tracing back the body from Cho Sing's at Forty-eighth Street to the Palace Gardens dance-hall region at One Hundred and Sixth Street, began a painstaking examination of all persons known to have been at the dance hall that night. While no clues within the dance-hall could be found, either on the roof or on window sills, the proprietors of the hall admitted that the evening had been disturbed by sounds as if of a brawl in the men's washroom a little after 2 a.m. It had quieted down quickly, and the proprietors had thought nothing of it, for such sounds were not un-common at the Gardens.

Captain Danforth put a young woman detec-tive on the case. She visited the Palace

Gardens frequently, posing as the jazziest of flappers, and within a week had learned two important facts. First, several of the girls who had frequented the place and might therefore have been in a position to testify as to events of the night had left town suddenly on Sunday. Second, there had been a Porto Rican chauffeur there that night—dark, handsome, and in a dress suit. No one could be found who had seen him go home.

Meanwhile the victim had been identified by the press as José Racheta, Porto Rican chauffeur and race-track devotee, temporarily out of work. Captain Danforth discovered that Racheta had entered the Palace Gardens alone, in the possession of $550 won that afternoon on a horse race. By tracing the girl habitués of the Palace Gardens to Boston, where they had been sent to get them out of the way, Captain Danforth was able to learn the names of two men seen to have entered the washroom after Racheta did so a little after 2 a.m. on that Sunday.

Both men were arrested in a car on Brooklyn Bridge eleven days after the finding of Racheta's body. In the pockets of Alexander Kargos, the elder, were found cuff links identified later as Racheta's. Petrino Guido, an

Italian window cleaner, living in the Bronx, was the other suspect. Both broke under the third degree and confessed to the robbery and murder of Racheta in the dance-hall washroom.

Quickly cutting out all identification marks from the clothes, Guido, the window cleaner, had clung to the window sill with his knees while he had leaned out and dropped the body on the "L" train as it sped by, scarcely two feet below and three feet away.

Captain Danforth was promoted and the murderers were electrocuted.

No. 4

THE PROBLEM OF THE FORGER'S TORN NOTE

1. The lounge of the Savoy Hotel was the place named in the note for a meeting of "Red" Sam Gunther's band. (Credit 5.)

2. Date of meeting—Wednesday noon. (Credit 5.)

Scotland Yard deduced this information

from the fragments of the torn note, which they reconstructed as follows:

Meet us Savoy
lounge prompt at
noon Wednesday

Plain-clothes policemen acquainted with the facts of Gunther's adherents were present in force and bagged four men long wanted by the authorities.

No. 5

THE SANDY PENINSULA FOOTPRINT MYSTERY

1. At the spot marked 2 on the diagram Mrs. Strang and her escort (woman and man) were strolling along the beach side by side when they were overtaken by Revington Strang on horseback. Strang evidently leaned down from his saddle, seized his wife, lifted her up on to the horse. Her escort (man) was forced to step aside to avoid being run down, as Strang's horse passed in front of him. (Credit 1.)

2. Man *ran* after the horse, then swerved up the beach toward the pile of rocks at 3 on the diagram, with the evident intention of hiding to observe the movements of the horseman. Then, noticing that the rider had almost reached the end of the beach, he waited to see what he would do. (Credit 1.)

3. At 3, noticing that the horseman had turned north toward the road, man turned and made a short cut to the road, knowing that the horseman would have to ride past him to leave the peninsula. (Credit 1.)

4. Near 4 man undoubtedly waited in the bushes for the horse to come, then leaped out, stopped the horse, and dragged the horseman to the ground. (No footprints showed on the macadamised road.) Presumably they fought in the road, as there were no footprints or other marks showing the struggle. Man presumably knocked Strang out by a terrific blow on the chin. Discovering that he had killed his adversary, man dragged the body underneath the bushes at the side of the road. Footprints around the body show that he dragged it by the feet, stood a moment looking at it, and then stepped to the side of the woman, Mrs. Strang, who was also standing looking at the body. (Credit 1.)

5. From 4 to 5 on the diagram there are no footprints of woman, but man's footprints, wide apart and pointing straight ahead instead of toeing out (compare man's footprints 1 to 2 with his footprints 4 to 5) indicate that he carried a heavy weight from 4 to 5. From 5 to 6 the footprints had undoubtedly been covered by the *incoming* tide, but the presence of the woman's footprints from 6 to 7 show that she must have been with man. Therefore it is possible to deduce that she might have fainted at 4, while looking at the body of her husband. She was being *carried* by man between 4 and 5. (Credit 1.)

6. Man carried woman down to the water, where presumably he revived her, near 5, by splashing water on her face. (Credit 1.)

7. Between 5 and 6 they walked along the sand near the margin of the sea, but their footprints had been covered by the *incoming* tide before the detectives arrived on the scene. (Credit 1.)

8. Between 6 and 7, where footprints of man and woman are again visible, they walked side by side, the closeness of the footprints showing that Mrs. Strang, still weak, was being supported by her escort. (Credit 1.)

9. At 7 their footprints are again covered by

the tide, but it is obvious that they returned to their starting point (somewhere seaward between 1 and 7), where they must have left their canoe, launched it and left the peninsula. The marks left by the canoe (necessarily pulled up on the sand) had been covered by the tide when the detectives arrived; but the testimony of the lighthouse keeper showed that a man and a woman had arrived by canoe. In all probability they left the peninsula in this way. (Credit 1.)

10. It can be deduced that the horse, after the event at 4 on the diagram, probably ran off down the road, for it left no footprints on the beach after once turning into the road. (Actually, the horse was found later in the fields near Parkville, several miles south of San Serena.) (Credit 1.)

The murderer of Revington Strang, undoubtedly Mrs. Strang's escort of that afternoon, was later identified by the detectives as Rupert Hardesty, a former welterweight champion of Yale University. Hardesty and Mrs. Strang never returned to England, fleeing that afternoon, it later developed, to the Continent, where they took passage on the ill-fated *Emerald Queen,* bound from Marseilles for

Yokohama. The *Emerald Queen,* it will be recalled, went down with all on board during the great typhoon of 1922, off the Japanese coast.

No. 6

THE CASE OF THE STOLEN VAN DYCK

1. Harry Sims, day attendant at the Farjeon Museum, wrote the ransom note about the stolen Van Dyck. (Credit 10.)

The detective cleverly identified the handwriting of Sims (as given in the application for a position) with the disguised handwriting of the ransom note.   Sims was arrested on suspicion; and later developments in the case brought about a confession.

Superficially it might even seem that the handwriting in the ransom note most nearly resembled that of Gregg, the night watchman, but on closer examination it will be seen that, good disguise as it is, several characteristic details were overlooked by Sims, most notably the crossing of the t's.   The crossings on his t's were not horizontal, but tended toward an arch in

style—an unusual and distinctive evidence.

Sim's handwriting, moreover, is obviously that of a person with considerable dexterity with a pen. And the writing in the ransom note, with its stiff and carefully made strokes, indicates that great pains had been taken to make it appear different from the natural hand of the writer. Neither Weaver nor Gregg show in their handwriting the excellent control of the pen that Sims has.

In attempting to disguise his handwriting, Sims forgot another point: he failed to eliminate from the ransom note his habit of breaking off the stroke in the midst of a word and then beginning with a new stroke. (See the space between the "pain" and "ting" in "painting," and between the "s" and the "t" in "strictly," etc.)

The *dénouement* of the Sims case is noteworthy in that it involved what was probably the first criminal catch effected jointly by aeroplane and radio. The museum trustees had taken precautions to have a radio sending apparatus installed in the rearmost first-class compartment of the train; and aeroplanes acting as patrols in the distant wake of the train.

Eighty miles out of the manufacturing town,

in the midst of a four-mile level spot, a man
with two yellow flags rose from behind a pile of
ties and waved to the end of the train. The bag
was thrown over promptly, and, to lessen suspicion, the train did not slacken speed, but
within ten seconds the alarm was being broadcast to listening radio stations all along the
route. The man with the yellow flags had
picked up the bag, opened and examined its
contents with satisfaction, and hurried down to
an adjacent lane, where an automobile stood
ready.

The police of the towns in the region were
prepared for quick response. Within ten
minutes six searching parties had begun the
hunt, and all roads for a radius of twenty miles
were being watched. Even so, it is probable
that the fugitive would have escaped had it not
been for the aeroplane then following the train
at a distance of three miles. Scouts with field
telescopes in the plane were attracted to the
general scene of the getaway and later spied a
car travelling at tremendous speed towards the
hilly country of the Welsh border on a rough
country road. By flying faster and in a more -
direct line, the aviators were able to outstrip the
car and drop messages in neighbouring towns.
The aviators lost the car in some woods, but by

landing quickly they were able to telephone directions to the local police which resulted in the capture of Sim's confederates with the money intact.

Sims confessed after brief questioning that he had cut the Van Dyck from its frame and smuggled it out of the museum in the arm of his raincoat on the evening of May 3rd, when the night watchman was late. His confederates included his second cousin and a former clerk in an art shop. The portrait was recovered in perfect condition from a safety deposit box in London, where the clerk had taken it the day following the theft.

Sims and his confederates were convicted and received heavy terms.

No. 7

THE WAYSIDE MYSTERY

1. The murder car had Dunlop Tyres, as was shown by the distinctive pattern of the tracks. (Credit 2.)

2. It could be deduced that there were at least two men in the car. The body of the girl had evidently been thrown out while the car was *in motion*. Doing this would almost cer-

tainly have required a driver plus the man who hurled the body. (Credit 2.)

3. The body had been there only a short time, for the dress and stockings were *splashed* with dew in several places. If it had lain there most of the night the clothing would have been soaked with dew all over, not splashed. (Credit 2.)

4. The car was travelling from east to west. The forward momentum of the body in the direction in which the car was travelling when the body was thrown out caused the bushes and twigs to be flattened out in that direction. (See illustration.) Also, the body was lying with the head toward the west. The fact that the skirt was comparatively smooth down over the legs also showed the forward momentum of the body toward the west. If it had been thrown out with its feet in the direction in which the car was travelling the skirt would have been blown up instead of down. (Credit 2.)

5. The missing slipper was not found near the body. Therefore, Constable Barge reasoned that it might have fallen off in the car at the time of the throwing of the body. If this had happened the slipper probably would have been thrown out later. A search along the road might locate the black patent leather slipper.

Tell-tale fingermarks of the murderer might logically be expected to have remained on its highly polished surface. (Credit 1.)

6. In the bushes along the road to the *west* of the place where the body was found would be the logical place to look first for the missing slipper, for the person throwing the body out of the car would probably wish to get rid of such damning evidence as quickly as its presence was discovered. (Credit 1.)

Soon after the discovery of the girl's body by Constable Barge, the family of Ada Smithson, a typist employed in a large business house in Southampton, informed the police of that town that she had disappeared.

The Smithsons were a respectable middle-class family, but their daughter, Ada, a girl of unusual beauty, had been in the habit, in spite of her parents' objections, of going out to cinemas and dancing places with men whom they did not know. The office in which she worked was that of a large steamship company, and hence she had the opportunity of meeting many birds of passage.

Lately, various friends had observed her in the company of a dark foreign-looking man who was staying at one of the best hotels in South-

ampton, and who had recently arrived from South America. He had disappeared the same time as Ada Smithson, and so had two Brazilian friends of his with whom he had often been seen drinking in the hotel bar.

It was the evening of the day before the discovery of the murdered girl's body that Ada Smithson had failed to come home. Her parents were confronted with the body and recognised it to be that of their daughter. The afternoon of the same day, a car with Dunlop tyres was found abandoned in a side lane between Southampton and Bournemouth. The police had already found that the fingerprints on the black slipper corresponded with fingerprints at Scotland Yard of a well-known Argentine criminal, called Miguel Sojos.

A detective who knew Sojos by sight traced him to Plymouth, where he had gone after abandoning the car, and arrested him just as he was stepping on board a vessel bound for South America. His Brazilian confederates were never found. Sojos broke down and confessed that he and his friends had kidnapped the girl, who suddenly realising what their intentions were, had started to struggle and scream when in the car, and she had been murdered and thrown out in the manner already related.

No. 8

THE DEATH THREAT CLUE

A mutilated copy of the *Saturday Review*, which was found in Paget's room, proved him guilty of sending the clipped-word death threat letter. (Credit 10.)

The word " Saturday " in the pasted note was in the distinctive style of type used in the words " *Saturday Review* " which are printed after the heading " Subscription Rates " on the front page of that publication. Observation of this fact had led the detectives to expect that a mutilated copy of this paper might be found in the room. The clipping fitted to the mutilated page.

Paget confessed, with more braggadocio than discretion, and was later sentenced to a term of imprisonment.

No. 9

THE SCULPTOR'S STUDIO MYSTERY

1. Reginald Lamont, the sculptor, was murdered by his wife. (Credit 2.)

2. Detective Coldstream deduced that the wife must have been in the studio on the afternoon of the murder. From the part of the word " ack " on the fragment of paper found in the fireplace and from the mesh design around the words, he believed that it was part of an envelope used as a container for a hair net. He found on investigation that it was, in fact, a part of the upper right-hand corner of a " Venida " hair-net envelope.

Hair nets are made in various colours and shades : Auburn, Blonde, Dark Brown, Black, etc. The " ack " could be only part of the word Black. Lamont's wife was a black-haired Spaniard; the other suspect, a blonde. It seemed highly probable, therefore, that the wife had lied when she testified that she had not been in the studio of the day of the murder. (Credit 5.)

3. The motive of the murderess was probably not only jealousy, but also revenge for an insult. (Credit 1.)

4. The head of the statue had been smashed, but no other part of the body. The wife, a woman of thirty-seven, had posed for the statue. The younger woman had recently posed for Lamont for a study of her head. Detective Coldstream deduced that the

sculptor, using as a model the study of the
head he had made of Miss Halverson, had
changed the face of the statue sometime after
the wife had finished posing, and that Mrs.
Lamont, coming unexpectedly to the studio,
had been infuriated by the discovery (especially
since she had probably heard of her husband's
relations with Helga Halverson). (Credit 2.)

Then, the detective reasoned, the wife had
snatched up the mallet in her anger and had
struck the head of the statue. Lamont interfered to protect his work and was attacked by
his wife in a frenzy.

Mrs. Lamont pleaded temporary insanity.
She admitted at the trial that she had come
unexpectedly to her husband's studio on that
afternoon. It was a windy day, and immediately upon entering she went to the mirror
above the mantel to smooth her hair. She then
recalled that she had in her bag a hair net, and
put it on, having discarded the envelope in the
fire at her feet. As she was finishing she caught
sight in the mirror of the changed face of the
statue, and, in her own words at the trial, " remembered nothing more until after the terrible
thing had happened."

The jury, however, did not believe it, and she is now in prison.

No. 10

THE BEALS-BLIGH ANONYMOUS LETTERS

1. Lady Beals-Bligh, Sir Chatham's wife, sent the anonymous letters. (Credit 2.)
2. This can be deduced from:

   (a) The American, rather than the English manner of spelling " dishonourable "—in the first letter. It was not spelled with a " u."

   (b) Somewhat similar misspellings in the first anonymous letter and Lady Beals-Bligh's forgiveness letter to her husband: " incontrovertable " instead of the correct " incontrovertible "; and, in the forgiveness letter, " seperate " instead of the correct " separate."

   (c) Similarity in style of construction of sentences in the first anonymous letter and the wife's forgive-

ness letter: long sentences with many hanging clauses. (Credit 5.)

3. Suzette, the French maid, was almost certainly the accomplice in the case. She probably posted the first letter in London and wrote the second from dictation over the telephone and posted it in Staines. (Credit 3.)

The private detective, former Inspector Givott of Scotland Yard, reasoned it out for his colleagues some years later as follows:

"Lady Beals-Bligh undoubtedly had heard the common gossip of Sir Chatham's renewed carrying on with the Austrian baroness. She loved her husband and wanted to end the affair without destroying his respect for her. *Open* charges against him, she believed, would mean the end of their marriage, so she hit upon the plan of frightening him by an anonymous letter.

"There can be no doubt that she prepared the first letter in Tirringham and sent Suzette to London with it for posting. This, Suzette must have done immediately upon her arrival in London on the morning of the day before Lady Beals-Bligh's town visit. She posted it at Paddington Station.

" After Suzette had gone, it must have occurred to Lady Beals-Bligh that the first letter was much more ominous in its sound than she had intended. She feared that her husband might turn it over to the police or do something desperate, fearing a *public* exposure. Therefore, she must have communicated with Suzette, who, I infer, was probably staying overnight at the well-known French hotel in Staines. It would have been natural for her to do so, since her mistress was coming to town the following day. (Undoubtedly they had made plans to meet in town.)

" The second anonymous letter was post-marked from Staines and was in a slightly different hand-printing. I believe, therefore, that Lady Beals-Bligh told Suzette to write a second letter and mail it immediately. This read: ' What I mean is, I will tell your wife if it does not stop.' That would limit Sir Chatham's fears and would indicate that no public exposure was intended.

" Lady Beals-Bligh and Suzette met in London the next morning and proceeded together to the town house, as if they had just arrived from Tirringham together. The wife must have been stunned when her husband confessed his infidelity. Her plan had worked so

beautifully for her that she was compelled to pretend that she would not forgive him. Or possibly she had hoped that the gossip was not true after all, and was really disappointed. At any rate, she probably intended even then to forgive him. She went back to their Tirringham place and did not let much time go by before writing him a letter from there, offering peace.

" As for Hobbs, I doubt that he knew anything of the matter. His presence in Staines must have been a coincidence, else he had never volunteered the information that he had been there. As a matter of fact, I later learned that Hobbs had met the innkeeper through friends of Suzette some months before. No doubt Suzette told the innkeeper to say nothing to anyone of her being at the inn, since she was supposed to be still at Tirringham. Of course, Hobbs guessed that Suzette had something to do with it the moment he saw the Staines postmark, but could hardly afford to voice suspicion of his fiancée to Sir Chatham.

" Naturally, when I saw how matters lay, I recommended to Sir Chatham's counsellor that we report a dead wall and advise dropping the matter. And I am told that they are still married."

No. 11

MESSER BELLINI'S REPORT
TO THE DOGE

1. Torcello was able to poison Geronimo alone, and not others, by a slight move of the thumb when pouring him a cup of wine from the pitcher. The vessel was designed for such a deed. Between the tiny hole in the flower blossom and the tiny hole under the lip of the pitcher ran a very narrow channel or tube *inside the clay of the pitcher*. This tube had been filled with poison. According to a law of physics, when Torcello kept his thumb firmly over the hole in the blossom, and poured, *wine only* went into the cup. But when he took his thumb off, poison began to trickle out. It issued from the hole under the lip of the pitcher and merged inconspicuously with the wine stream.

Since the movement of control was almost imperceptible to even a suspicious observer, the Cavaliere's villainy was not easily detected. The accident of Baptista's blowing under the lip of the pitcher revealed the existence of a hole there and a hole in the blossom where the bubble appeared. She had blown back some

remaining drops of the poison. (Credit 5.)

2. If Baptista had helped herself to wine from the pitcher she would probably have been poisoned. Presumably her hands were much smaller than Torcello's, and it is not likely that she would, entirely by accident, press her thumb against the flower with the little hole. (Credit 2.)

3. As far as the person making the report (Messer Bellini) was able to deduce, the pitcher was made with an open fretwork around the neck, except the part near the lip of the pitcher (see illustration), in order to make the working of the device more certain. If the wine were poured out fast, there might not be time for a sufficient dose of poison to mingle with the stream of wine. Obviously, the fretwork was a cunning contrivance designed to force the pourer to pour slowly, or to make slow pouring appear natural. If the wine were poured swiftly, it would naturally come in such a wide stream that it would spill through the open-work. The open-work therefore somewhat aided the murderer in masking his infernal design. (Credit 3.)

Messer Bellini's report to the Doge closes with an elaborate description of the pitcher

and urges the arrest and imprisonment of the Cavaliere Torcello. It is interesting to note that Doge Arbasini agreed, casting the murderer into the famous dungeon of the Doge's Palace and later having him dragged head downward through the streets at the tail of a horse—a favourite Venetian method of execution.

The origin of the poison pitcher could probably be traced far into antiquity, although this is, so far as is known, the first record of the amazingly ingenious device. Later these pitchers became quite popular in Venice.

No. 12

THE MYSTERY OF THE MURDERED PHYSICIAN

1. The murderer of Dr. Winthrop Brett was a woman. (Credit 1.)

2. This was proved by the single sheet of newspaper found lying in front of the radiator. Inspector Marquard deduced that the long, narrow, shrivelled mark on the page must have been made by the drying of a damp stocking. He reasoned that the murderess reached over

the body to get the little green books from the wall safe; that in so doing her stocking came in contact with the large bloodstain on the breast of the doctor's coat. He knew that in 1926 skirts were worn very short and that stockings were usually light in colour. (Credit 9.)

"Unable in any way to *hide* the damning stain on her stocking," Marquard writes, " and knowing that the valet would not return until six, she removed her stocking, washed out the stain, and went to put the stocking along the top of the radiator where it would dry quickly. Seeing the newspaper near-by, she tore off a page, laid it on top of the radiator, and laid her stocking along it so that the stocking would dry without any dirt or rust from the radiator—a very natural action. She would probably have had to wash almost the whole leg of the stocking, for silk stockings show very plainly any marks left by water.

" After the stocking had dried and she had removed it from the radiator, the piece of newspaper was wafted off the radiator by the hot air rising from it; or possibly she carelessly knocked it off when removing the stocking.

" The fact that she had left the cold water

running also pointed to her having washed away a blood-stain, for cold water is much preferable to hot water for removing blood-stains.

"It may be argued that a woman, under these circumstances, would scarcely have dared to run the risk of lingering in the apartment long enough to wash her stocking; but to appear on the street without having done so would be far more dangerous. She had no way whatever of hiding the conspicuous stain. To wash and dry the stocking sufficiently to permit wearing it would take less than twenty minutes. Moreover, very soon after she had killed the physician she must have realised that her shots had not been heard, for no one came running. She probably had been intimate with Brett and probably knew that there would be no other appointments that afternoon but her own. For I cannot doubt that she was the person who telephoned at 11 p.m. and then overheard the doctor release Wilkins till six.

"It is also obvious that the murderess was in a mood for playing a desperate hand, for when she failed to force the physician (perhaps at the pistol point) to *give* her the books, she shot him and took them.

"As to her identity, of course I know

nothing; but it seems probable that she had been one of the doctor's patients, that she had at some time made indiscreet confessions to him, of a personal nature, which he had recorded and possibly used to obtain a hold on her. And that she finally rebelled is certain.

"I should imagine that the 'little green books' have been long since destroyed, and that the lady's identity will never become known."

No. 13

THE AFFAIR OF THE FRENCH
SPY

1. Mlle. G., the French spy, communicated the message to her confederate in the dot and dash of international Morse Code hastily embroidered as clocks on ordinary plain silk stockings. (Credit 7.)

2. The message read:

Left leg . . . .   − . . .
          H   B

Right leg . . − − −   − . . . .
         2   6

HB26 was the secret-service number of the treacherous spy that the French were seeking. (Credit 3.)

Although it is not recorded whether or not Mlle. G. knew that her confederate could read the code, this would seem unnecessary, since she might at least be certain that he would observe and copy the design and have it decoded later.

No. 14

THE SHOOTING OF
"WHISPER" MALLOY

1. "Long Dan" Shutz killed "Whisper" Malloy. He shot with the Enfield rifle from ambush on the north side of the road. (Credit 2.)

2. The unknown man killed "Long Dan" Shutz. He shot with the Winchester rifle from ambush on the south side of the road after Shutz climbed into the car. (Credit 2.)

3. "Whisper" Malloy must have been shot first. (Credit 1.)

4. The body of "Long Dan" was found in "Whisper" Malloy's car because, after killing

Malloy, he rushed from his ambush and jumped
into the car to prevent it from running wild,
which it had started to do (see motor-car
tracks).   Probably he had righted the wheel
and was starting to turn the bend in the road
when he was struck by the unknown man's
bullets.   (Credit 3.)

5. The unknown man went to the car to
plant his Winchester near " Whisper," in order
to give the impression that the two men had
fought a duel.   He removed his finger-prints
from the Winchester.   (Credit 2.)

Though the unknown man was never caught,
the police were confident that it was but one
more incident in the history of the country-
house burglars which was disturbing the community.   They explained matters as follows:
It was well known in the underworld that
Shutz was out to get " Whisper."   The unknown must have been a member of the burglar
gang which was at war with Shutz because he
had not played fair with them over the
matter of disposing of some stolen property.
" Whisper " had heard of Shutz's threats
against him and was on his way to Southampton to catch a vessel sailing for abroad.   Shutz
had heard of this plan, and decided to lie in

wait for him. The unknown also heard how matters stood, and determined to catch Shutz while the American criminal was catching the informer. From the south side of the road the unknown watched the unsuspecting Shutz waiting behind the tree on the north side for the approaching car of the informer. The unknown then shot Shutz as described and planted the evidence.

He could then walk away from the scene unarmed, leaving the stage set as if a desperate duel had occurred.

No. 15

THE PROBLEM OF NAPOLEON'S SIGNATURES

1. The signature as General in Chief of the Egyptian Expedition was B: "Bonaparte." This was done in 1798, when Bonaparte was only twenty-nine years old. He had been successful as a soldier, but his character had not formed as in the signature of 1806 (D). The unsettled or unformed nature of the writing (compared with D) and the fact that he signed "Bonaparte" instead of "Napo-

(Continued on page 42)

B

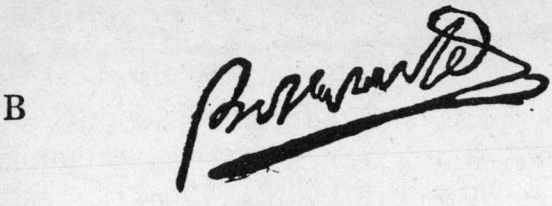

Written as Chief of the Egyptian Expedition in 1798.

H

Done very soon after becoming Emperor, in 1804. Age 35.

D

Done at Berlin, October 29, 1806. At the very height of his career. He was still thinking clearly. Egotism had not yet dominated.

G

At the Imperial Camp at Tilsit, 1807, when the Emperor had virtually all Europe, except England, at his mercy. Perhaps the climax of his military successes, but the beginning of his tremendous egotism.

F

Done October 1, 1813. Bonaparte's enemies were slowly but surely wearing him down. Several of his armies commanded by his marshals had been defeated. Yet he was not to be beaten decisively until 1815.

A

A few days before his abdication as Emperor (just before voluntary exile on Elba). Done April 4, 1814.

C

September, 1814. From the island of Elba.

E

Done two months after arriving at St. Helena on his forced and final exile. Date December, 1816.

leon " should indicate the identity of the signature.   (Credit 2.)

2. The signature when he first became
Emperor in 1804 was H.   This is written
" Napoleon " (he chose to become known as
Napoleon I.).   It resembles somewhat B.   He
had not yet developed the complete mastery
of himself that is to be seen in D (1806).
(Credit 3.)

3. The signature at Tilsit was G: a mere
" N." It is sweeping, triumphant, masterful.
This was in 1807. Compare with the indecision
of F signature (six years later) when his defeat
was threatened.   (Credit 2.)

4. The signature at Elba was C.   It shows
clearly the breaking down of the man and his
fortunes, yet it has some dash.   It lacks the
resignation of the St. Helena signature, E.
(Credit 2.)

5. The St. Helena signature is E—note how
the capital N has slumped down almost to the
level of the smaller letters.   Compare it with
the virility of the D signature, which was done
ten years before.   (Credit 1.)

The various signatures, in their chronological
order, on pages 40 and 41 tell a rather obvious
story of the rise and fall of Napoleon Bonaparte.

No. 16

THE GREAT IMPERIAL BANK ROBBERY

1. The tyre tracks which at first baffled Elkins were clearly those of an aeroplane.

The robbers had confederates in an aeroplane circling over the road to Derham, waiting for their car. When the pilot caught sight of the car, perhaps identifying it through some prearranged signal, he came down and landed in the road some distance in front of it. The car then came up behind, and the robbers transferred the loot, their guns, and the clothes in which they had committed the robbery into the aeroplane. The width between the tyre tracks compared with the width of the motor-car tracks indicate an aeroplane. The narrow tyres, without markings, and the mid-track made by the metal tail skid of the machine, are also characteristic. (Credit 7.)

2. A detective would in all probability radio a general alarm for aeroplanes seen anywhere in the vicinity, try to learn the direction each had taken, where it had landed, and make a

thorough check - up of all such machines.
(Credit 3.)

No. 17

THE PROBLEM AT THE
ABANDONED BUNGALOW

1. In all probability there were four men in
the gang at the abandoned bungalow. This is
indicated by the number of cups, and by other
clues which follow. (Credit 2.)

2. The man who sat in the chair in the right
foreground of the illustration was probably a
tall man with a sore or wounded foot. From
the illustration it will be seen that the chair on
which the bottle of iodine stands is in a direct
line with this chair, and from the direction in
which the latter chair is turned it is possible to
deduce that the man who sat in it was using
the other chair as a foot rest. The chairs were
not very near together, so the police deduced
that it was a *tall* man who had the sore foot.
Probably his neighbour at the left had been
dressing the wound for him and had placed the
iodine on the nearest edge of the chair used for
a foot rest.

This man to the left must have been a pipe

smoker, judging from the large number of burned *wooden* matches around his chair. Many pipe smokers prefer the larger and longer burning flame of wooden matches to the short-lived paper ones.

The man at the back of the table (in the illustration) was evidently left-handed, as is indicated by the position of his cup with relation to his chair.

The man who sat on the wooden box and drummed with his heels, making the dents in the box, was an unusually short man, or at least had very short legs, as shown by the distance of the dents from the top of the box. He probably was short in the trunk also, as he evidently chose the high wooden box to sit on. The cigar butt found by the cup at this place indicated almost certainly that the short one was not a woman. (Credit 8.)

No. 18

THE WARFIELD-COBHAM
JEWEL ROBBERY

1. The butler was an accomplice in the Warfield-Cobham jewel robbery. (Credit 1.)

2. The advertisement which the detective took from the " Situations Wanted, Male," column was really a message in cipher. Taking every sixth word in the advertisement, the message reads:

Back bureau northwest second business offers opportunity Wednesday twelve.

The detective saw that this message constituted directions for robbing Mrs. Warfield-Cobham's home. " Back bureau " obviously meant " back of the bureau," the location of the wall safe in the widow's bedroom. Americans and Canadians call a dressing-table a " bureau," and say "back of " for " behind." " North-west second " must have referred to the location of the room, which was the north-west room on the second floor. The rest of the message indicated that Wednesday midnight would be a favourable time. (Credit 9.)

Ardmore was arrested that night at the Warfield - Cobham house, and " Gentleman Claude " was caught two weeks later in London. Both men were convicted and given long sentences. As to his reasons for employing the devious method of communication with his confederate, Ardmore later explained as follows to the police:

" It wasn't my idea, but Claude was afraid to call for letters anywhere, and he feared that a telephone or telegraph message from the house would be traced to me. I never thought of doing anything like this, but Claude had heard about the stuff [the jewels] being bought, and he said he could handle the job alone if I would just tip him off and let him in."

Ardmore had had a good record, according to the police, until he had fallen under the influence of " Gentleman Claude " a year previously. The use of the newspaper want advertisement as a cipher appealed to " Gentleman Claude " as safe and amusing.

No. 19

THE LA JOYA RIVER HOMICIDE

1. Search for further clues should have been directed to the Gordon Ranch. (Credit 10.)

Since the victim had been strangled before immersion, his body may have assumed to have floated and drifted with the current on the east side of the river, which ran at a speed of six miles per hour. Since the hands of the watch,

when examined, pointed to 5.25 (and it had
been recently wound up and therefore had been
running) ; and since the immersion tests with
similar watches indicated that the water caused
it to stop within two to four minutes, the time
of the body striking the water may be assumed
to be about 5.21 or 5.23.

The body was sighted going over the mill
dam at 6.13. It had therefore been floating
down for fifty or fifty-two minutes at the rate
of six miles per hour. It would therefore have
travelled approximately five miles or a little
more. The river, being free from impediments,
can be assumed to have brought the body down
from a distance of five miles. Measuring back
on the map it is apparent that the Gordon
Ranch's *north-west* corner is just five miles
from the dam. Had it come from the Wilson
or Cosgrave Ranches, the body would have
arrived at the dam much later or sooner.

The murderer was never caught. The police,
unfortunately, became confused and tried the
Smith Ranch, which proved a dud. Later, on
the Gordon Ranch they found the footprint
record of a scuffle, but were unable to fasten
the crime on anyone in the vicinity. Molly was
held guiltless.

No. 20

THE DUVENANT KIDNAPPING CASE

1. The kidnapper's car departed downhill, to the south.   (Credit 3.)

2. Conclusive proof of the direction taken by the car is to be seen in the close-up drawing of the stud impressions in the tyre track.   It will be noted that in each stud the impression is sharper (that is, more deeply imprinted) at the end toward the bottom of the hill.   It will be seen from the close-up of the tyre track *on the level* that the impressions are of the same sharpness (that is, depth) at *both ends*.

Had the impressions of the studs been deeper at the end toward the *top* of the hill (the reverse of the way they were found), they would have indicated that the car had come uphill from the south and gone north.   (Credit 7.)

This interesting subtlety in detective work is described by Melville Davisson Post in his excellent book, *The Man Hunters*.   Mr. Post says:

The Swiss police authorities assert that the direction taken by an automobile cannot be determined on a level road; but if one will fol-

*low an auto track until it begins to " descend
a grade," he can determine the direction the
car has taken on the grade, provided the tyres
be studded. . . . As the car " descends" the
hill the " anterior" part of the studs on the
tyre will be imprinted a little more deeply than
the posterior part, or they will seem deeper by
reason of the compression of the earth under
the weight of the car on the studs as it
advances.*

*Thus, to discover the direction taken by a
motor car one has only to follow the track to a
grade and there ascertain whether it is the
anterior or posterior part of the studs of the
tyre that are deeply imprinted on the dust,
snow, or mud of the road.*

By following the kidnapper's car downhill to
the south, Norcross and Duvenant were able
to pick up the trail from various A.A. scouts
and attendants at petrol-filling stations. It
led direct to the South - Western Hotel at
Southampton, where Mrs. Duvenant was just
leaving for the boat. Jonathan was with her,
and so was her father!

To Duvenant's surprise, his wife's father
insisted upon her returning the child at once,
but Duvenant compromised, upon the father's

signing a bond guaranteeing the safe keeping and return of the child, by letting her keep him for a week's visit. It is understood that the matter was settled out of court.

No. 21

THE LIGHTHOUSE TRAGEDY AT DEAD MAN'S HARBOUR

1. There could be only two explanations of the mystery at Dead Man's Harbour. Either the captain had deserted his post or he had met with foul play. M. Jacques believed the latter because he deduced that whoever had *left* the island by foot had taken pains to conceal his footprints, which he had done by dragging a board over them. The fact that this board had been dragged, obviously to efface footprints, since not a trace of a footprint remained, pointed to concealment and indicated a strong motive for mystifying the townspeople. The captain's boat was still on the island, so he couldn't have left in it. He had not been seen in the town, and there was no evidence that he had departed voluntarily. If the captain had suddenly become a victim of amnesia and had wandered off into the woods, he would hardly

have taken the precaution to conceal his footprints. Everything considered it looked like
foul play, especially since M. Jacques saw that
a murderer could have done his deed, disposed
of the body, and escaped, as will be seen later.
(Credit 1.)

2. The murderer had probably reached the
island in a boat on the incoming tide the night
before—in all probability before eleven when
the fog settled down. (Credit 2.)

3. The murderer disposed of the body of
Captain Williams by putting it into the boat
in which he had come to the island. He left
the oars in the boat and set it adrift just as
the tide began to go out again, knowing that
the rush of the outgoing tide would carry the
boat out to sea. A forty-foot tide necessarily
moves *rapidly,* and the murderer took advantage of this. Undoubtedly he had planned to
take the body off in his boat, but dared not risk
getting lost in the fog. (Credit 2.)

4. The murderer escaped from the island by
walking over the damp sand at low tide (dragging the board behind him to destroy footprints
which otherwise would have indicated the direction taken). By so doing he completely mystified the local authorities. The murderer would
undoubtedly have left the island much sooner,

perhaps wading when only shallow water remained, except for the dense fog which hung over the region. It is probable that he did not feel certain of finding his way in the fog to the ladder—the only means of ascent to the promontory at low tide. (Credit 3.)

5. The captain's body probably would be found in the boat, which might be picked up at sea by some vessel, or along the coast by fishermen. (Credit 2.)

Thirteen days after the disappearance of the captain a dead man in a small boat was picked up twenty-five miles out by a freighter *Water Nymph*. It was that of Captain Williams. He had been shot through the heart.

The small boat was brought to port. The name had been painted out, but careful removal of the obliterating coat of paint disclosed the name *Dodger*. This rather unusually named boat enabled the police to find and investigate its owner, a former seaman who had lived in the little town of Eastport, Maine, for the previous ten months, doing odd jobs for the fish canneries there.

They found that the seaman, Jacobs, had sailed under Captain Williams on the captain's last voyage, more than twelve years before.

The records showed that he had headed a mutiny which had been sternly put down by the captain. Several of the mutineers had been killed; Jacobs and two others had been brought home in irons and tried. Jacobs had received ten years in the Federal penitentiary. He confessed when cornered (having turned up in the police line-up at Pennsylvania) that ever since his release he had been shadowing Captain Williams to " get him."

Jacobs was executed.

No. 22

WHO MURDERED ALGERNON ASHE?

1. Frederick Freeman, the American, husband of Mary Freeman, murdered Algernon Ashe at Monte Carlo. (Credit 1.)

2. The detective deduced it from the burned fragment of cardboard which he recognised as part of a dated weight card from a penny-in-the-slot machine. The Monte Carlo detectives had previously reasoned that this was probably drawn from the murderer's own pocket when he was in urgent need of something to ignite from his waning last match.

Proceeding on this hypothesis, the famous detective deduced that the " 16-6 " on the fragment (meaning 16 stone, 6 lbs.) fitted only Freeman. He alone of the men of the three suspected parties was tall and stout, according to the descriptions gleaned from the hotel attachés. It was more reasonable, therefore, to follow the Freemans to Paris than the others to Spain and Rome. (Credit 9.)

The printing on the back of the weight card also served to identify it. It appeared as possibly a part of the stereotyped " character reading " which weighing machines all over England, notably in the Woolworth stores, commonly give for a penny in addition to one's weight. Stout persons, keeping close tabs on their variations in weight, are frequent patrons of such machines. In this case the whole of the back of the card would have read: " You are studious and have a good sense of humour. You appreciate wit and satire. Thus your work is made agreeable." The Freemans had spent several weeks touring in England before coming to Monte Carlo, and the card was stamped 'Peerless Weighing Machine Company, London.' "

It came out subsequently that Freeman had

suspected an affair between his wife and Ashe and had intercepted a letter to her sent that afternoon by the Englishman. The jealous husband had opened the envelope with a hot knife, had read the letter, and restored it to the envelope, and gummed down the flap again, so that his wife had no suspicion of the tampering. In the note Ashe had named a tryst for that evening in the gardens to discuss final plans for a proposed flight to India or Brazil. The tryst was for 9.30, a time of the evening when Freeman would customarily be at play at the casino tables.

Freeman said nothing. He went to the casino as usual but left early, and told his wife that urgent business demanded their presence in a Paris bank by the next day. He promised a quick return, however, and she, rather than arouse his suspicion, consented and began immediately to pack for the journey to Paris. Freeman then left to keep the appointment and shot down Ashe in cold blood. As he afterward admitted, Freeman searched the body hurriedly for letters from his wife, which he thought Ashe might be carrying in his pockets. He found three, which subsequently served to draw the net tighter when they were found in his possession.

Mrs. Freeman, when she wrote to Ashe explaining her inability to keep the appointment, feared to send the letter by messenger and mailed it instead. This the detectives got the next morning at Ashe's hotel.

Freeman was convicted, but escaped with a nine-year sentence. Mrs. Freeman sued successfully for divorce, and later married a French architect of Marseilles.

No. 23

EDOUARD TRIMPI'S PERPLEXING DISPATCH

1. Trimpi had cleverly evaded the Spanish censorship and was therefore arrested, when it was discovered, by the Spanish authorities. (Credit 5.)

2. The gist of the *Chronicle's* scoop was: a revolution in Spain is imminent because of public discontent with the royalist government, and there has been a military outburst resulting in the capture of several hundred of the royalist soldiers who were trying to bolster up the government's position. It is unlikely that the fall of the royalist government can be averted because the populace is with the armed rebels. (Credit 5.)

Trimpi's position at the beginning of the outbreak in Barcelona was tantalising. He happened to be there and happened to get the
details of the important occurrence, but could
send no news of it to his paper because of the
strict government censorship which obtains.
Therefore Trimpi took a chance on couching
his dispatch in veiled language which might
appear unimportant routine to the Spanish
censors, but would probably convey the news
to his newspaper. By pretending that he was
interviewing himself on technical financial
details of stock-market affairs he succeeded in
doing this once, but was caught and arrested
the second time.

Trimpi used " complete market overturn "
for " revolution "; " accumulated lack of
popular buying of *chair* shares " for " long
growing discontent with the *throne* "; " sharp
rise of steel " for " armed outbreak "; " operators " for " soldiers "; " curb buying with steel
as favourite " for " popular support of the
armed rebels."

When the editors of the *Chronicle* heard
from the State Department of Trimpi's arrest,
they comprehended the significance of his
cable.

The revolution was unsuccessful, although for a time it seemed almost certain to succeed. Trimpi was released a week later upon request of the State Department, after promising not to attempt evasion of the Spanish censorship again.

No. 24

THE CLUB CAR MYSTERY AT SYRACUSE

1. To locate Dennis Sloan, the brakeman of the train, a search should have been ordered for his dead or wounded or senseless body along the railroad line, probably *east* of Ford's Crossing. (Credit 3.)

2. Sloan's arrest as murderer of Capewell should *not* have been ordered. Sloan was undoubtedly a victim of the escaped murderer, as it is evident that the murderer *impersonated* the brakeman when Osborne tried to enter the car. (Credit 2.)

3. Sloan was not an accomplice. (Credit 1.)

4. The murderer, not Sloan, must have assaulted the porter. (Credit 2.)

5. In all probability, after the last call to dinner in the club car, at 7.30, Capewell and

one other passenger (the murderer) remained in the car, as well as Johnson, the porter, and Sloan, the brakeman—the latter probably on the back platform, where a brakeman often stands. The murderer probably black-jacked the porter and brakeman, and then followed out his well-laid plan of murdering Capewell and throwing his body off the train.

The brakeman either fell off accidentally or was thrown off by the murderer, *after* the murderer had taken his coat and cap to wear in impersonating the brakeman before Osborne, the passenger. The murderer undoubtedly escaped by jumping when the train slowed down. He left the coat and cap, poorly concealed, to throw suspicion on the brakeman, though this was probably an afterthought. (Credit 2.)

Captain McCumber has commented as follows on the case:

"It's an unsolved mystery to-day because the detectives didn't recognise immediately that someone in the club car was impersonating the brakeman when Osborne tried to get in the club car. This should have been clear from two things: the 'brakeman's' answer when Osborne asked him the time—'eight of eight.'

(No railroad man would have said that; he would have said, ' 7.52.') Also, the coat and cap in the drawer; if Sloan had wanted to hide them, he would have thrown them out of the train; obviously they were left there for a purpose: to throw some suspicion on the brakeman, or rather, to leave something which might be taken to explain what had happened.

"The real murderer, of course, jumped from the back platform when the train slowed down on approaching the yards of Syracuse. On the outskirts of the city is where they should have looked for him. Instead of that, they leaped to the conclusion that Sloan had done it, and all the while poor Sloan was lying in the gully beside the embankment near Orrington with a broken leg and a bruised skull. Some track walkers found him two hours later.

" I later questioned both Sloan and Johnson, the porter, soon after their recovery, but, of course, it was too late then: the murderer had had plenty of time to get away.

"On the basis of what Sloan and Johnson told me, I reconstructed the happenings as follows:

"The murderer had undoubtedly planned the crime, hoping to get Capewell alone on the back platform, shoot him, and throw him off

at a time when the train was about to slow down. This would give him a chance to drop off with comparative safety and escape. Capewell, it seems, had had an early dinner and returned to the club car. Possibly he was dozing.

"The murderer was probably unknown to Capewell, or was disguised. Soon after the other passengers went forward to the diner, he went to the front of the club car, where Johnson was looking out of the window, and struck the unsuspecting porter with a blackjack. All Johnson remembered was that something hit him from behind. Johnson could not tell me how many passengers had remained in the club car after the last dinner call.

"Taking the porter's keys, the murderer locked the front door of the club car and drew down the curtain in its window. He then hurried, for he knew that passengers might be returning and seeking entrance to the car at any minute. Sloan, standing on the platform, was also struck from behind. He remembered only that. I imagine that the murderer then lured Capewell to the back platform, possibly by calling out that the brakeman had fainted and needed assistance; and when Capewell came to the platform and bent over the brakeman, shot him and threw his body off.

" The murderer then heard the pounding and ringing of the impatient Osborne at the front door of the car. The train had not yet slowed down, but was due to slow down soon. From the murderer's point of view, therefore, it was imperative to stave off any investigation of the locking of the car, which might have resulted if the passenger had become disgusted and summoned a conductor.

" Guessing that it was a passenger, but not feeling sure, the murderer stripped the prostrate brakeman of his coat and hat, donned them and *peeked* out from behind the door-window curtain. When he saw that it was a passenger and not one of the train crew (who would have known him for an impostor), he unlocked the door and put Osborne off by saying the car was temporarily closed. To have refused an answer to Osborne's question: ' What's the right time?' would have aroused more suspicion than to answer him. He did so, therefore, but not as a railroad man would certainly have said it. But this, of course, was lost on Osborne, and unfortunately on all of those who first investigated the case.

" I am inclined to the belief that the murderer, upon re-locking the door and rushing to the back platform, found that the brake-

man had fallen off from the swing of the train;
but possibly he was more cold-blooded than I
imagine and threw the unconscious brakeman
off.   At any rate, he saw the advantage of
leaving the brakeman's coat and cap in the
drawer, thereby implying that the brakeman
had tried to conceal them.   The train slowed
down a few minutes later, and he undoubtedly
jumped off and made his escape.

" It was one of the most cold-blooded and
carefully planned murders I have ever investigated."

No. 25

THE MYSTERY OF HAJI LAL DEB

1. Mainwaring deduced Haji Lal Deb's
probable guilt from his deception as to the
time of the death of his aged relative. It seemed
highly probable to Mainwaring that there must
have been a *strong* motive for anyone to hold a
plague-stricken body for two days before burying it.   The coincidence of the holding of the
body for burial and the disappearance of the
rich merchant was highly suspicious.   It indicated that Haji Lal Deb might have postponed

burial of the body in order that the event might mask some other operation. And Mainwaring reasoned: Haji Lal Deb knew that holding the body was a suspicious act; therefore he lied and said that his relative had died *on the very night* of the disappearance of the merchant. (Credit 4.)

2. Mainwaring proved the guilt of Haji Lal Deb by digging up the ground directly *under* the body of the relative. There, four feet below the grave of the old man, lay the corpse of the merchant. (Credit 6.)

Haji Lal Deb had sought to fool the authorities and avert all suspicion by hiding the merchant's body in the one place where they would be the least likely to look for it after examining the topmost grave. He was immediately arrested and charged with the crime, and, although he protested his innocence, was convicted and executed.

Autopsy revealed that the merchant had been drugged with *dhatura,* an insidious Indian poison as easily made there as dandelion wine could be made in England. The *dhatura* flower is common in India, growing wild in the fields. A small dose of *dhatura* will stupefy the victim so effectively that he loses memory temporarily

and can later tell nothing of what happened while under the influence of the drug. A large dose is fatal. It was substantially proved at the trial that Haji Lal Deb had drugged the merchant with *dhatura* mixed in a bowlful of rice, and had subsequently robbed him and stabbed him to death. Two hundred and forty rupees were later recovered from a cache under the roots of a wild plum tree in the vicinity of the hut of Haji Lal Deb.

In Mainwaring's opinion, the death of the aged relative of his wife suggested to Haji Lal Deb a neat way of disposing of another body without much suspicion. He accordingly planned the murder of the merchant for robbery—a crime which, Mainwaring believed, he had long contemplated.

Charges against the wife as an accomplice broke down for lack of evidence.

No. 26

THE STRANGE CASE OF THE PROMISSORY NOTE

1. The markings on the back of the yellowed document led Mrs. Mannington to suspect that

something might be wrong because they were obviously *part* of some design which had been cut off of the sheet of paper. And if something had been cut off, it was reasonable to suspect that it might have been cut off for the purpose of concealment. (Credit 3.)

Mrs. Mannington noted especially that the only part of the mysterious markings remaining on the back of the piece of paper almost coincided with the position of the signature on the reverse side. These markings had to remain on the back if the signature on the reverse side was to remain. She suspected that otherwise they would have been cut off also.

2. In the opinion of all the lawyers and of Mrs. Mannington, Rannard had probably obtained the piece of paper from his deceased sister's autograph album which Mannington had at some time undoubtedly signed. (Credit 7.)

This they deduced cogently from the strange pen-and-ink markings on the back of the sheet on which the alleged promise to pay had been typed. In these finely stroked lines they recognised ends of pen strokes such as were used in making the elaborate "flourish" designs often inscribed in autograph albums in the latter part of the last century. In such

albums some wrote verses; some " flourished "
intricate designs of birds, flowers, etc.; some
even painted little water-colours; and those of
lesser accomplishment merely signed their
names, with date.   Richard Mannington had

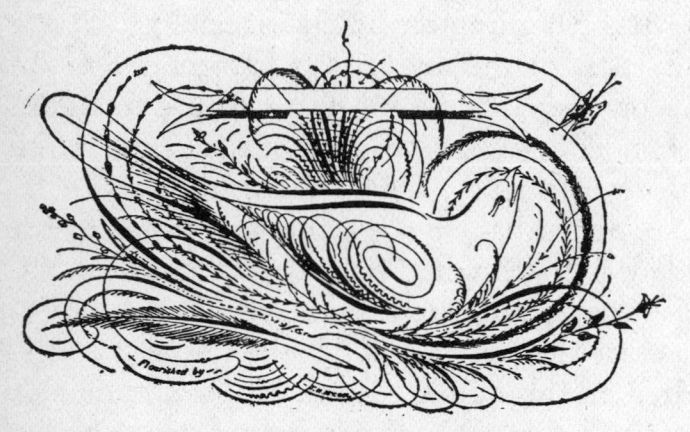

A   typical " Flourish "—complete

*An accomplishment of ladies and gentlemen during the Victorian
era. Some of the designs were extremely elaborate and required considerable dexterity, for the work had to be done rapidly in order to
achieve the desired dashing effect. The best " flourishers " were in
great demand by every girl who possessed an autograph album, and
most girls of that day had one*

been of this latter class.   He had probably
signed his name and the date in the centre of
a page in the album.   The person next invited
to inscribe in the album had " flourished " a
design on the other side of the sheet, and it
happened that the fringe of one side of the

design nearly coincided with Mannington's signature on the reverse.

When Mr. Philip Rannard fell into possession of the album upon his sister's death, he probably saw in it an opportunity to forge a note over the signature of Mannington now grown wealthy. When Mannington died, the opportunity to prey on his widow became obvious to him. He clipped the page from the album and trimmed it down as much as he dared; then he typed in the " note."

Rannard was never caught. The police found that Rannard had consulted typewriting experts some months before as to the characteristic type on typewriting machines used in the early 'eighties. He had bought an ancient machine from one of the experts, saying that he desired it for his private museum of business appliances. With this Rannard undoubtedly forged the typed lines of the " note."

No. 27

THE DEATH OF BARNABAS FROBISHER

1. Barnabas Frobisher met his death at the hands of the butler, John Graves. (Credit 5.)

2. This is rather conclusively indicated by the powder marks on the backs of the victim's fingers (which preclude the theory of suicide) and by Graves's own denial of the possibility that an intruder could have slipped in and murdered Frobisher. Graves wanted it to look like suicide and set the stage accordingly, but did not notice the tell-tale powder marks on the backs of Frobisher's fingers. These, of course, indicated that Frobisher, threatened at close range, had clapped his hands over his eyes when he saw that escape was impossible. The powder had been blown into the skin of the backs of the fingers. Such marks would have been impossible if Frobisher had fired the revolver, and barring that, only Graves could have murdered Frobisher and set the stage. (Credit 5.)

A letter from Frobisher to his wife found in the slain man's strong box later revealed that he was being systematically blackmailed by Graves for considerable sums of money, and that he was mustering his courage to have his persecutor arrested. Graves, alias George Rhonda, a professional blackmailer, had secured proof of a serious violation of the Income Tax law by Frobisher some years before, and had taken a position as butler to

be near his victim. He was so successful in intimidating his employer that more than £2,000 in cash had been paid by Frobisher. More had been demanded. Frobisher demurred. Graves had served an ultimatum for that evening. Frobisher told him to go to hell, and added that he was through with him. Fearing that he had oppressed his victim so far that the worm was about to turn, and knowing how heavily blackmailing was punished, Graves seized the opportunity offered by the absence of the others from the house and the driving away of the car, which would drown noise of the shot, and killed Frobisher without warning.

As he later confessed when captured at the station, Graves removed his shoes in the pantry, stole up on his victim who was reading, and shot him from the front. For this purpose he had taken Frobisher's own pistol from his bedroom upstairs. The butler then wiped his own fingerprints from the weapon, pressed it into the dead man's hand to register his fingerprints, and then laid it carelessly on the side of the seat of the chair. He then returned to the pantry, put on his shoes, walked in and out as if to discover the body, and then reported the crime to the police as a case of suicide.

Graves's insinuation to the police that Fro-

bisher had committed suicide because of losses from speculation was cogent, since Frobisher, hiding his troubles from his wife, had been obliged to assign speculation as an explanation for his heavy spendings (for hush money). Graves played his whole game secure in the knowledge that there was a complete absence of apparent motive for the crime. Had it not been for the powder marks on the backs of his victim's fingers, he might have escaped the constant shadowing which resulted later in his arrest as he was preparing to leave for London.

Graves was convicted the following April and was hanged.

No. 28

THE HUPPENHEIMER MUSEUM ROBBERY

1. Two men were guilty in the Huppenheimer Museum Robbery. There is no evidence that more than two were guilty. (Credit 2.)

2. Assistant Curator Raymond was the directing genius of the robbery; Antonio Diaz, whose coat was captured, was his confederate

who did the actual taking of the real gems.
(Credit 3.)

3. The robbery was carried out in the following manner:

On the day of the Prince of Wales's visit the
Assistant Curator deciced Curator Waltham.
He did not remove the real jewels to the safe,
but *left them in the case*. He put the paste
replicas in the safe and falsely reported to the
curator that orders had been carried out as
given.

Diaz, the confederate, made his appearance
the following day and began copying the design
of the Rurik jewels in order to make a dummy
set. Diaz was also studying the case and the
"lay of the land" on the second floor of the
museum.

Diaz was not yet ready for the robbery when
the Assistant Curator was suddenly ordered to
New York by Curator Waltham on an emergency errand. This fitted in splendidly with
the Assistant Curator's desire to avoid any
tangible suspicion of complicity: the robbery
should be done in his *unexpected* and *involun-
tary* absence, and then he believed that he
would scarcely be suspected of having a hand
in it. But he must let Diaz know.

Therefore, as soon as the Assistant Curator

received orders to go to New York immediately, to be gone from Friday until Tuesday, he dispatched instructions to his confederate in their prearranged code, to hurry and take advantage of the situation.   (Credit 2.)

4. Guilt was proved by Raymond's code message, ingeniously contrived to appear as an innocent column of figures.   It was probably tapped off on an adding machine available in the museum executive offices.   The code was a numerical one, and the message read:

Ordered N. Y. till Tuesday Strike soon.

The letters of the alphabet were numbered 1 to 26, starting at Z, and printed two letters to a line with a decimal point between, except where two numbers lower than 10 came together and would make a number larger than 26, when they were written as one number: for instance, 7 (T) and 6 (U) were written as 76.   Detective Wagner deciphered the message as follows:

12- 9-23-22-9-22-23   13- 2   7-18-15-15
 o r d e r e d   n y   t i l l
7- 6-22- 8- 23-26- 2   8- 7- 9-18-16-22
 t u e s d a y   s t r i k e
8-12-12-13   (Credit 3.)
 s o o n

Assistant Curator Raymond hanged himself in his cell the day following his arrest, and "Antonio Diaz" was never found. His identity, however, was learned, and this threw some light on the strange affair. "Diaz" was none other than Porfirio Butler, scapegrace son of Dr. Simeon Butler, the English-Argentinian gem expert and one-time director of the Buenos Aires Public Museum. Together, the foreigner and Raymond had probably planned the sale of the celebrated pieces under some ingenious guise—possibly to some South American museum or to a wealthy private collector.

It was the essence of Raymond's scheme to have the robbery appear to have been done by an outsider. Trading on his reputation, which up to that time had been good, the Assistant Curator would say that he had not mixed the real and false gems—and what could be done about it? At the worst his superiors could accuse him of carelessness. This he would deny vigorously and leave in any detective's mind the implication that any one of the three men who had the combination of the safe might have been an accomplice. But his confederate's carelessness in keeping the coded note in his coat pocket proved their downfall.

Curator Waltham resigned, a broken man. Dr. Oddie, however, exonerated him of all blame. It later developed that Raymond had been something of a Dr. Jekyll and Mr. Hyde. Several persons who had been the victims of forgeries at Raymond's hands during his youth came forward when the scandal came out.

The Rurik pieces were never entirely recovered. Three of the smaller amethyst rings were found in a London pawnshop some years later; and two of the large gold bracelets turned up in a private collection in St. Louis.

They are now kept in the museum safe *all* the time.

THE END